new success

Elementary
Workbook

David Riley
Rod Fricker
Dominika Chandler

CONTENTS

Exam Strategies   3

Functions Bank   6

Unit 1   Person 2 person   8

Unit 2   What a day!   14

Self-Assessment Test 1 Units 1–2   20

Unit 3   Looks good   22

Unit 4   Work   28

Self-Assessment Test 2 Units 3–4   34

Unit 5   My place   36

Unit 6   Eat up!   42

Self-Assessment Test 3 Units 5–6   48

Unit 7   I remember…   50

Unit 8   What's new?   56

Self-Assessment Test 4 Units 7–8   62

Unit 9   Great service?   64

Unit 10   On the road   70

Self-Assessment Test 5 Units 9–10   76

Unit 11   Body and mind   78

Unit 12   Look to the future   84

Self-Assessment Test 6 Units 11–12   90

Exam Vocabulary   92

Exam Vocabulary Practice   102

Exam Vocabulary Practice Answer Key   114

Self-Assessment Tests Answer Key   115

Self-Assessment Tests Tapescripts   116

strategies

The *New Success Workbook* provides practice with the most typical exam tasks found in upper secondary school-leaving exams as well as exams like PET, KET, FCE, Trinity and PTE (Pearson Test of English). The exercises are graded to elementary level to help students familiarise themselves with exam task types. The *New Success Workbook* includes exercises that will help you prepare for all parts of a typical exam: Listening comprehension, Reading comprehension, Grammar/Use of English, Speaking and Writing.

Listening comprehension

General guidelines

Always

- read the instructions carefully before listening to a recording for the first time. Try to predict what kind of information you might hear.
- look at the questions and mark your answers when listening for the first time.
- read through all the questions again before the second listening, paying special attention to the questions you didn't answer during the first listening.

Don't

- panic if you don't understand everything. You don't have to understand the whole text to be able to find the correct answer to a question. Try to get the main idea of a text and work out the meaning of words you don't know from the context.
- spend too much time thinking about questions you are not able to answer – you can come back to those during your second listening.
- leave any questions unanswered. If you are not sure – make a guess.

True/False (e.g. page 53, exercise 2)

- The questions are usually given in the same order as the information in the text.
- When deciding whether a sentence is true or false, take into account what you actually hear and not what you know or think.
- Sometimes you need to refer to the whole recording to answer a question, particularly when answering a question about the speaker's intentions.

True/False/No Information (e.g. page 24, exercise 2)

- Follow the guidelines for a *True/False* task, but remember that this time you have three options to choose from: a statement could be true (include the same information as the text), false (include information different from the text) or there might be no information regarding the statement in the listening task.

Multiple choice (e.g. page 39, exercise 1)

- The questions are usually given in the same order as the information in the text.
- While listening for the first time, make notes of possible answers. Then compare them to the options you have been given and choose the most similar.
- Some incorrect options sound very similar to the information in the recording – be careful and pay special attention to synonyms and antonyms.
- Sometimes the information needed to answer a question is not directly given, you may have to work it out on the basis of what you have heard. If you are not sure which answer is correct, try to choose it by eliminating the incorrect answers.

Matching (e.g. page 53, exercise 1)

- If you have to find out who a person is or where the recording takes place, concentrate on typical phrases which relate to the person or place. Sometimes one characteristic phrase will help you choose the right answer.
- If you need to match a text/passage to a summarising sentence/title/headline, try to summarise the main idea yourself and then choose the answer that is the most similar.

Answering questions (e.g. page 24, exercise 3)

- Read the questions carefully before you start listening, and try to predict possible answers.
- You are usually required to answer each question with no more than three words.
- The questions are usually given in the same order as the information in the text.

Completing sentences (e.g. page 81, exercise 2)

- The gapped sentences are given in the same order as the information in the text.
- Read the sentences carefully before you start listening and try to predict what kind of information you should be looking for. Usually, the words that you need to complete the gaps are exactly the same as the words used in the text.
- If the rubrics specify the number of words you should write, make sure your answers are the right length.
- Remember that your answer must be meaningful and grammatically correct.

Reading

General guidelines

Always

- read the instructions before doing the task. The task will affect the way you read the text.
- try to work out what kind of text it is – it may give you some ideas of what to expect.
- read key information first. A title helps to decide on a general idea of the text and the first sentence of each paragraph often summarises the whole paragraph.
- underline parts of the text relevant to the questions (single words, phrases, sentences, paragraphs).

Don't

- try to understand every single word of a text. You don't have to know all the words to answer the questions. You may be able to guess the meaning of new words from the context.
- leave any questions unanswered – if you are not sure, make a guess.
- spend too much time on one specific exercise – your time in the exam is limited.

True/False (e.g. page 17, exercise 2)

- Read the questions carefully before you read the text. Then skim the text to get a general idea of where the information is.
- Different questions will require different reading strategies. For example, you may need to focus on just one phrase or you may need to interpret the meaning of a whole paragraph.
- If you don't find information confirming that a particular sentence is true, mark it as false.

True/False/No Information (e.g. page 52, exercise 3)

- Follow the guidelines for a *True/False* task, but remember that this time you have three options to choose from: a statement could be true (include the same information as the text), false (include information different from the text) or there might be no information at all regarding the statement in the text.

Multiple choice (e.g. page 11, exercise)

- Identify the parts of the text that your questions refer to.
- Focus on the detail of a paragraph or sentence. An incorrect answer may only differ from the correct one in the tense that is used, slightly different information or information that only partly corresponds with the text.
- Eliminate incorrect answers and then mark your final answer.

Matching (e.g. page 25, exercise 4)

- While matching headlines to a text, always read all the headlines first and then match them to the relevant parts of the text.
- While matching questions to a text, try to find the place in the text where there is the answer to a particular question.
- Remember that this kind of exercise may include (an) extra sentence(s), so you will have to eliminate unnecessary items.
- When you match missing sentences to gaps in the text, skim the text first, ignoring the gaps to get its general meaning. Then try to complete the gaps with the missing sentences or words, paying special attention to what comes before and after the gaps.

Answering questions (e.g. page 58, exercise 2)

- Read the questions carefully before you start reading the text, and try to predict possible answers.
- You are usually required to answer each question with no more than three words.
- The questions are usually given in the same order as the information in the text.

Completing sentences (page 25, exercise 3)

- The gapped sentences are given in the same order as the information in the text.
- Read the sentences carefully before you start reading the text, and try to predict what kind of information you should be looking for.
- If the rubrics specify the number of words you should write, make sure your answers are the right length.
- Remember that your answer must be meaningful and grammatically correct.

Writing

You may be required to write a short, practical piece of writing such as a note, an email, an invitation, an advertisement and/or a longer, practical piece of writing, for example a formal or an informal letter, a story or a discursive text. The *Success Workbook* will help you prepare for these types of writing tasks. Remember that the exam techniques that you learn, even at elementary level, will help you pass exams successfully in the future.

General guidelines

Always

- read the instructions carefully – what kind of writing task is it?
- read the information you need to include in your writing.
- write a plan detailing information you want to include in each paragraph. If you have time, write a draft copy or a few key sentences.
- check that you have included all the information that is required. Use linking words so that your writing is coherent and logical.
- check your writing style – have you used formal or informal language as required?
- check (if it is a longer text) that you have an introduction, a middle and an end. Also, check that you have clearly defined paragraphs and that you have the correct number of words.
- check your grammar and spelling.

Don't

- write more than the word limit. Think about the number of words you need for each paragraph when you write your plan.
- repeat yourself – try to use varied vocabulary and grammar structures.

Speaking

The *New Success Workbook* will also prepare you for oral exams. The techniques below will help you to pass your exam successfully.

- Try to stick to the aim of the task. Always keep the question in mind when answering.
- Do not panic if you cannot remember a word. Use a word that has a similar meaning or give a definition or description of the word.
- If you do not understand what an examiner has said, ask him/her to repeat him/herself. You can also repeat the information you have been given and, in this way, you can make sure that you have understood it correctly.
- If you are not ready with your answers and need time to think, use conversational fillers or hesitation devices (*well, let me think, erm, ...*).
- Avoid using the same words and structures – show that you have a varied vocabulary and can use a range of grammar structures.
- If you are taking the exam with another person, make sure you listen as well as speak – don't dominate the conversation.

Functions bank

On the phone (Unit 1)

Saying hello
A: Hello, Kate here.
B: Hi Kate, it's James.

A: Hello. 442 7634.
B: Hi. This is Andy. Is that Jane?

A: Good morning/afternoon. Bike World.
B: Hello, is Julie Black there, please?

Saying goodbye
Bye./Bye bye./Goodbye.
See you soon/later/tomorrow/on Friday/at 7.
Take care.

Greetings
A: Hi Sue, how are you?
B: Great/Fine/Not bad, thanks. And you?

Other expressions
Sorry?
Sorry, wrong number.
Sorry, he's not here.
Hold on/Hang on a minute, please.
Just a minute/moment, please.

Expressing preferences (Unit 2)

I like/love helping my mother.
She enjoys school holidays.
I don't like eating a lot.
They hate getting up early.

Describing people (Unit 3)

Appearance
He's … and he's got …
He looks like …
They're both …
He doesn't look like …

Personality and interests
He's friendly and confident.
He is like …
They're both …
We both love music and reading.
She's very good at …
I like … but she doesn't.

Permission (Unit 4)

Asking for permission
Can I … , please?
Could I … , please?

Yes response
Yes, of course. No problem.
Yes, that's fine. Here you are.

_No_ response + reason
Sorry, I'm afraid not. That's my cup.
No, I'm sorry. That seat's not free.

Directions (Unit 5)

Asking for directions
Excuse me, is there a … near here?
How do I get to … ?

Giving directions
Walk past …
Take the first turning on the right.
Turn right at the traffic lights.
There's a bank on the corner …
Walk straight on.
Go to the end of the road.
… is on the right.
It's opposite the …

Buying food and drink (Unit 6)

The customer says:
Can I have … , please?
Have you got any … ?
I'd like … , please.
How much is that?
That's all, thank you …
Here you are.

The shop assistant says:
Can I help you?
Certainly. Anything else?
There's one left.
There are two left.
That's £3.50 (altogether), please.
Here you are.

Giving and receiving news (Unit 7)

Good news
A: You look happy.
B: Yes, I passed my … !

A: How was your day?
B: Great! I got …
A: That's brilliant!

Well done!
Good for you!
How fantastic!

Bad news
A: What's up? You look sad.
B: I failed my … !

A: What's the matter?
B: I lost my …
A: Oh dear!

I'm so sorry.
Never mind.
It doesn't matter.
Forget about it.
Don't worry.

Describing objects (Unit 8)

What does it look like?
It's … with …
It's in good/bad condition.
It looks modern/old-fashioned/nice/horrible.

How big is it?
What size is it?
How long/wide/high/thick is it?
It's smaller than your bag.
It's quite small/not very big.
It's 35 by 30 centimetres/metres.
It's about 3 centimetres long/wide/high/thick.

Other features
How heavy is it?
What make is it?
How much is it?
It weighs (about) 3 kilos/500 grams.
It's a Mikro/an Anwa.
It's £300.

Information (Unit 9)

Asking for information
Could you tell me … ?
Can you give me some information about … ?

Offering help
How can I help?
Shall I … ?
I can … , if you like.

Checking information
What do you mean by … ?
Sorry, did you say … ?

Suggestions (Unit 10)

Asking for suggestions
What can I … ?
What do you suggest?
What should I … ?

Making suggestions
If he likes … , you could get …
What about … ?
Why don't you … ?

Responding to suggestions
That's a good idea.
Yes, why not?
I don't think so.
I'm not sure about that.

Describing photos (Unit 11)

It's a picture of a …
I can see … people.
The younger boy is carrying a …
They've just …
On the left/right there is a …
Maybe it's the weekend and they're having a day out.
I think they're a …
They look …

Opinions (Unit 12)

Giving opinions
I think it's horrible/terrible/great/wonderful.
I don't think it's a very good idea.
In my opinion, you should complain about it.
Personally, I don't think it'll make any difference.

Agreeing
Yes, I (completely) agree.
Yes. I agree with you.
Yes, you're (absolutely) right.

Disagreeing
Sorry, but I don't agree.
I'm afraid I disagree.
That's true but …
I know what you mean but…

 **Person 2 person**

GRAMMAR

to be affirmative and negative

	Affirmative	Negative
I	**am ('m)** on holiday.	**am not ('m not)** at home.
He/She/It	**is ('s)** in Budapest.	**is not (isn't)** in Prague.
We/You/They	**are ('re)** Italian.	**are not (aren't)** Spanish.

> **Mind the trap!**
>
> We use *to be* to talk about age.
>
> She's twenty-one. (NOT ~~She has twenty-one.~~)

Possessive adjectives

Subject pronouns	Possessive adjectives
I	my
you	your
he	his
she	her
it	its
we	our
you	your
they	their

1 Complete the sentences with the correct form of the verb *to be*: affirmative (+) or negative (–).

Tom <u>is</u> from Paris. (+)

1 We _____ good friends. (–)
2 I _____ an English student. (+)
3 Kevin and Ali _____ on holiday in Brazil. (+)
4 China _____ a very big country. (+)
5 I _____ a doctor. (–)
6 You _____ twenty-one. (–)
7 Jenny _____ at school today. (–)
8 They _____ good students. (–)

2 Use the verb *to be* and the words below to write full sentences.

We / not in Spain / We / in France
<u>We aren't in Spain. We're in France.</u>

1 She / not English / She / American
_____

2 I / not at home / I / at a party
_____

3 You / not a teacher / You / a student
_____

4 It / not from France / It / from Hungary
_____

5 They / not my brothers / They / my cousins
_____

3 Choose the correct word.

Hi! *My̲* / I / I'm name is Lisa. *My* / I / *I̲'̲m̲* from Brighton.

1 These are my friends. *Their / They / They're* names are Charlie and Helen.
2 Charlie's great. *He / His / He's* seventeen years old.
3 *He / His / He's* parents are doctors.
4 Helen is my best friend. *She / Her / She's* family is Spanish.
5 *They / They're / Their* from Valencia.
6 We are students. *We / We're / Our* school is in Green Street.
7 *It's / Its / It* a big school.
8 *It / It's / Its* name is Green Street High School.
9 What's *you / your / you're* school called?

4 Complete the text with the correct subject pronouns or possessive adjectives.

This is a photo of <u>my</u> friend, Jenny. She's from England, but ¹_____ parents are Russian. This is ²_____ house in Brighton. ³_____ is very big! She's with ⁴_____ boyfriend. ⁵_____ name's Dale.
This is me with ⁶_____ mum and dad. ⁷_____ are on holiday. This is ⁸_____ house in Spain. And this is my brother and ⁹_____ girlfriend in Paris. ¹⁰_____ dad's an English teacher at a high school there.
Now you show me ¹¹_____ photos!

GRAMMAR

to be questions

Yes/No questions and short answers

Yes/No questions			Short answers
Am	I		Yes, I **am**. No, I**'m not**.
Is	he she it	**Japanese?**	Yes, he/she/it **is**. No, he/she/it **isn't**.
Are	you we they		Yes, we/you/they **are**. No, we/you/they **aren't**.

Mind the trap!

Saying just *yes* or *no* can be impolite.
Say *Yes, I am* or *No, I'm not*.

We say *Yes, I am*. (NOT ~~Yes, I'm.~~)

Wh- questions

What is your name?
Where are you from?
How old are your parents?
Who is your teacher?

---

1 Match the questions with the answers.

Is Mark Smith English? ☐ b

1 Is Maria Spanish? ☐
2 Is Liverpool in Yorkshire? ☐
3 Where is Oxford? ☐
4 Are you and your friends Italian? ☐
5 Are Louise and Andy your friends? ☐
6 How old is your house? ☐
7 Who is James Stevens? ☐
8 Are you seventeen? ☐
9 What is your dad's name? ☐
10 Am I a good student? ☐

a Yes, they are.
b ~~Yes, he is.~~
c No, we aren't.
d It's about fifty years old.
e Yes, I am.
f No, it isn't.
g His name's Richard.
h No, she isn't.
i He's my English teacher.
j Yes, you are.
k It's in England.

2 Choose the correct word.

Am / Is / (*Are*) you from Italy?

1 *Is / Am / Are* I your cousin?
2 *Am / Is / Are* Warsaw in Poland?
3 *Am / Are / Is* your friends on holiday?
4 *Is / Am / Are* your brother fifteen?
5 *Is / Am / Are* you Hungarian?

3 Make *Yes/No* questions and complete the short answers. Use the words in brackets and the verb *to be*.

Are you married? (you/married)
Yes, I am.

1 _____ (he/Turkish)
Yes, _____ .
2 _____ (they/in Kiev)
No, _____ .
3 _____ (you/twenty-one)
No, _____ .
4 _____ (she/on holiday)
No, _____ .
5 _____ (you/students)
Yes, _____ .

4 Choose the correct question word.

(*What*)/ *Who* is his name?

1 *How / What* old is she?
2 *Where / What* are they from?
3 *What / Who* is your boyfriend?
4 *Where / What* is her address?

5 Write *Wh-* questions for the answers below.

Where are you from?
I'm from Belgrade.

1 _____
My name's Dragana.
2 _____
I'm seventeen.
3 _____
My phone number is 91 329 778.
4 _____
My best friend's Adrijana.
5 _____
She's from Novi Sad.

GRAMMAR

Possessive 's

Singular nouns: add 's
Sally's husband's a doctor.

Regular plural nouns: add '
This is my parents' house.

Irregular plural nouns:
The children's school is in the centre of town.
The men's names are Peter and Luke.

Mind the trap!

My brother's friends = one brother
My brothers' friends = more than one brother

We say John and Sally's daughter (NOT ~~John's and Sally's daughter~~)

Both the verb *to be* and the possessive *'s* can look the same:

Mark's brother = possessive *'s*
Mark's eighteen = is

1 Look at the family tree. Complete the sentences.

Philip + Elizabeth

Charles   **Anne**

Philip is <u>Elizabeth's</u> husband.

1 Elizabeth is _____ wife.
2 Charles is _____ brother.
3 Charles and Anne are _____ children.
4 Anne is _____ sister.

2 Choose the word with the possessive 's.

John's Peter's brother.

1 John's wife's French.
2 Annie's John's wife.
3 Annie's dad's a doctor.
4 Sophie's Annie's mum.
5 John's mum's Helen.
6 Helen's husband's Mike.

3 Match the pictures with the sentences.

1 This is a picture of my sister's sons. ☐
2 This is a picture of my sisters' sons. ☐

LISTENING AND SPEAKING

1 [T2] Listen to the conversation and write the phone numbers.

Name:	Nick Green
Home:	1 _____
Work:	2 _____
Mobile:	3 _____

2 [T3] Listen to the telephone conversation. Choose what the people say.

Receptionist World Music. (Good morning)/ Good afternoon.

Anne Hello. Is Simon Parke there?

Receptionist ¹*Hold on / Hang on a minute,* please.

Simon Hello.

Anne ²*Hello / Hi* Simon. ³*This is Anne / Anne here / It's Anne.*

Simon Hi Anne. How are you?

Anne ⁴*Very well / Fine / Not bad,* thank you. And you?

Simon I'm OK.

Anne Simon, where's John this week?

Simon He's in Tokyo.

Anne Oh, of course. Thanks. See you ⁵*soon / later / tomorrow* then.

Simon See you. ⁶*Bye / Bye Bye / Goodbye.* Take care.

Anne Bye.

3 [T4] Put the conversation in the correct order. Then listen and check.

a Bye. Take care. ☐
b Good morning. World Music. ☐ 1
c Hang on a minute. It's 07789 233 066. ☐
d Hello Marlene. This is Tom. How are you? ☐
e Hello. This is Marlene Katz. Is Patty Vincennes there? ☐
f Hi Tom. I'm fine, thank you. And you? ☐
g No problem. What's her mobile number? ☐
h Thanks very much. Bye, Tom. ☐
i Very well, thanks. But Patty isn't here today. She's in London. ☐

READING

1 **T5** Read and listen to the article. Choose the best title.

A Celebrities' children's names

B Celebrities' names

C My children's names

What's your name? Is it traditional or is it unusual? Celebrities often give their children unusual names.

Brooklyn, Romeo and Cruz. Brooklyn is a part of New York, Romeo is the hero of Shakespeare's play, *Romeo and Juliet*, and Cruz is a beautiful, traditional Spanish girl's name. They are also the names of David and Victoria Beckham's three sons. Yes, sons. Cruz isn't their daughter. He's a boy, too.

Zuma Beach is in Malibu, California, home of many film and music stars. Nesta is reggae singer Bob Marley's middle name. Rock is a kind of music. That's why singer Gwen Stefani and rock star Gavin Rossdale's second child is called Zuma Nesta Rock. His brother's name is Kingston. Kingston is Bob Marley's home town in Jamaica. Is Bob Marley Gwen and Gavin's favourite singer?

Finally, there is a children's TV character called Ben Ten. It is a nice name because the words rhyme. But rhyme is not so good for pop star David Bowie's son. His name is ... Zowie Bowie!

2 Read the article again and choose the correct answer.

1 Cruz is Brooklyn's
  a brother. b sister. c son. d daughter.

2 Romeo's mother is
  a Victoria. c Spanish.
  b Juliet. d from New York.

3 Bob Marley's full name is
  a Bob Nesta Marley.
  b Bob Kingston Marley.
  c Bob Zuma Marley.
  d Bob Malibu Marley.

4 Kingston is a
  a girl. b singer. c father. d boy.

5 Zuma is Gwen's
  a daughter.
  b son.
  c favourite singer.
  d husband.

6 David is Zowie's
  a father.
  b favourite TV character.
  c brother.
  d son.

WORD LIST

Countries and nationalities
American
Australia
Brazil
Brazilian
Britain
China
Chinese
Egypt
Egyptian
England
English
France
French
German
Germany
Hungarian
Hungary
India
Indian
Italian
Italy
Japan
Japanese
Mexico
Poland
Polish
Russia
Russian
Spain
Spanish
Turkey
Turkish
the USA

Family members
aunt
brother
children
cousin
daughter
father/dad
grandchildren
grandfather
grandmother
grandparents
grandson
husband
mother/mum
nephew
niece
parents
sister
son
stepfather
stepmother
uncle
wife

Describing a photo
at home/school/a barbecue/
    a party
in a classroom/garden/café
in the middle
next to
on holiday
on my left/right

Personal information
address
age

(first) name
married
phone number
single
surname

Other
accommodation
actor
be called
beautiful
big
birthday
boy
boyfriend
care (take care)
classroom
day
doctor
dog
door
double (adj)
everything
excuse me
family
family tree
favourite
form (n)
friend
friendly
girl
girlfriend
here
hold on/hang on
host family
hostel
house
international
job
language
language school
life
little (adj)
local
love (v)
man/men
month
new
nice
people
person
please
question
railway station
sorry
speak
street
student
student hall
summer school
sunglasses
teacher
teenager
(tele)phone (n)
there
university
week
weekend
woman/women
wrong number
young

12

VOCABULARY

1 Write the opposites of these words.

dad   mum
husband   1 _____
2 _____   daughter
3 _____   niece
uncle   4 _____

2 Complete the crossword with family words.

ACROSS
1 Your daughter's children are your…
3 Your grandparent's children are your…
8 Your father's brother's daughter is your…
9 Your father's grandchildren are your…
10 Your father's mother is your…

DOWN
1 Your mother's father is your…
2 Your brother's son is your…
4 Your sister's daughter is your…
5 Your mother's brother is your…
6 Your father's son is your…
7 Your mother's daughter is your…
11 Your father's sister is your…

3 Write the plurals.

man   _men_
1 woman   _____
2 child   _____
3 person   _____

4 Choose the odd one out.

doctor / teacher / friend / student

1 French / Turkey / Spanish / Chinese
2 at home / at university / at school / at half past six
3 on the right / on holiday / on the left / in the middle
4 women / men / children / family
5 in a garden / in London / in a classroom / in a café

5 Write the headings from the box in the correct place on the form. There is one extra word that you don't need.

| Address Age Country Married ~~Name~~ |
| Nationality Single Surname |

Hi. I'm Lisa Rossi. I'm from Rome. I'm 19 and I'm not married.

UKvisas

Name: Lisa
1_____: Rossi
2_____: 19
3_____: ☐ 4_____: ☒
5_____: Italy
6_____: Piazza Danti, 7a, 001856, Rome

6 Write the nationalities.

Brazil — Brazilian
1 China — _____
2 Poland — _____
3 France — _____
4 Germany — _____
5 Hungary — _____
6 Spain — _____
7 Japan — _____
8 Italy — _____
9 Turkey — _____
10 Russia — _____

7 Complete the text with *in*, *at* or *on*.

These are three photos of me and my family. This is me with my sisters. We're <u>in</u> the garden 1_____ home. I'm 2_____ the middle, Kate's 3_____ my left and Nicola's 4_____ my right. Our brother John isn't in the photo. He's 5_____ university 6_____ Edinburgh. Oh, and this photo is of me and John 7_____ holiday. We are 8_____ a café 9_____ Amsterdam. And this one is me and Kate 10_____ school.

WRITING | Capital letters

1 Add capital letters to the email.

| NEW MESSAGE ☒ |

From: maria@world.coo
To: Annie Benson
Subject: Hi!

hi annie,

how are you? i'm on holiday, i'm in london with jane

and her family. their house is beautiful – it's near the

university. jane's dad's english but her mum's hungarian.

she's a teacher and he's a doctor. they're great but her

brother's stupid. his name's david and he's thirteen.

this is a photo of jane and me. we're near oxford street.

london is beautiful in july!

jane sends her love.

see you next monday,

maria

xxx

02 What a day!

GRAMMAR

Present Simple: affirmative and negative

	Affirmative	Negative
I/You/We/They	**live** in Prague.	**do not (don't) live** in Prague.
He/She/It	**lives** in Prague.	**does not (doesn't) live** in Prague.

We use the Present Simple for things which are true most of the time:
- facts about your life: *I **work in an office**.*
- routines: *I **get up** at six thirty every day.*
- generalisations: *Children **like** sweets.*

The spelling rules for *he / she / it* are:
- for most verbs, add an *s*: *get – get**s**; move – move**s***
- for verbs ending in *-o, -ss, -sh, -ch, -x* add *es*: *go – goes; finish – finishes*
- for verbs ending in a consonant + *y*, change *y* to *i* and add *es*: *study – studies, try – tries*
- there is one irregular verb: *have* becomes *has*

1 Choose the correct spelling.

Larry [visits] / *visites* his grandmother on Saturdays.

1 My dad *gos / goes* to work by bus.
2 Steve *plays / plaies* computer games in his room.
3 Natalia *does / dos* a lot of sport.
4 My mum *tidys / tidies* our bedrooms.
5 Oliver *cooks / cookes* great meals.
6 Paula *haves / has* breakfast at school.

2 Read what Emma says and complete the sentences about her.

My name's Emma. I'm English but I live in New York. I work in a library. I start work at ten thirty in the morning and finish at about seven in the evening. I get home late – about eight. I have dinner at home. After dinner I watch TV – I really like American TV.

She <u>lives</u> in New York.

1 She _____ in a library.
2 She _____ work at ten thirty in the morning.
3 She _____ work at seven in the evening.
4 She _____ home late.
5 She _____ dinner at home.
6 She _____ TV after dinner.
7 She really _____ American TV.

3 Make affirmative and negative sentences using the verbs from the box.

~~watch~~   start   finish   ~~work~~   get   live
have   like

My brother <u>watches</u> TV all the time. (+)
My dad <u>doesn't work</u> in an office. (−)

1 I _____ dinner at school. (−)
2 My friends _____ listening to music. (+)
3 My mum _____ work at seven in the morning. (+)
4 My English teacher _____ in a big house. (−)
5 We _____ school at 4 o'clock in the afternoon. (+)
6 Mark and Julia _____ home late. (−)

4 Make the sentences negative and write the correct information using the words in brackets.

Cathy lives in a small house. (big house)
<u>Cathy doesn't live in a small house. She lives in a big house.</u>

1 We get up at seven in the morning. (six)
_____

2 My parents have breakfast at home. (at work)
_____

3 John works in a school. (an office)
_____

4 I work seven hours a day. (nine)
_____

5 You go to bed at ten o'clock. (at midnight)
_____

6 The library opens at nine o'clock. (ten)
_____

GRAMMAR

Present Simple: questions

Yes/No questions and short answers

Yes/No questions			Short answers
Do	I you we they	**like** music?	Yes, I/you/we/they **do**. No, I/you/we/they **don't**.
Does	he she it		Yes, he/she/it **does**. No, he/she/it **doesn't**.

Mind the trap!

We don't add *s* to the verb in third person questions.

Does she work? (NOT ~~Does she works?~~)

Wh- questions

Where	**do**	I you we they	**live?** **work?**
	does	he she it	

What do you do after school?
Who do you sit next to in class?
When do you do your homework?
Which film do you want to see?
How do you go to school?
Where does your mum work?

---

1 Complete the questions and short answers.

> <u>Do you go</u> (you/go) swimming at the weekend?
> No, <u>I don't.</u>

1 _____ (he/get up) early on Sundays?
No, _____

2 _____ (they/work) in an office?
No, _____

3 _____ (she/go) to parties?
Yes, _____

4 _____ (you and Kara/chat) on the Internet?
Yes, _____

5 _____ (this bus/go) to the city centre?
No, _____

2 Complete the questions for these answers.

> What <u>time does she get up</u>?
> She gets up at seven o'clock.

1 What _____ ?
I have coffee for breakfast.

2 Where _____ ?
We live near the university.

3 How _____ ?
My brother goes to school by bus.

4 When _____ ?
My parents get home from work at seven in the evening.

5 Who _____ ?
At the weekend, I meet my friends.

6 Which _____ ?
I want to buy the new U2 CD.

3 Complete the dialogue with the correct questions.

A Can I ask you a few questions?
B Yes, of course.
A <u>Do you live</u> near here?
B Yes, I do. I live in that house there.
A <u>Who do you live with?</u>
B I live with my mum, my dad and my brother.
A ¹_____
B Yes, we do. We go to Park School.
A ²_____
B We go to school by bus.
A ³_____
B My dad works in an office and my mum is a teacher.
A A teacher?
⁴_____
B She teaches French.
A ⁵_____
B No, she isn't my teacher. My French teacher's name is Mrs James.
A ⁶_____
B In my free time I like meeting my friends, going to the cinema, watching TV… lots of things.
A ⁷_____
B Yes, I do. I play football, I go swimming and I play tennis.
A Great! That's all, thank you!
B No problem.

GRAMMAR

Adverbs of frequency: *always, usually, often, sometimes, never*

We put the adverb of frequency before the main verb in the Present Simple:
> She **always gets up** early.
> I don't **usually eat** in restaurants.

We put the adverb of frequency after the verb *to be*:
> We **are never** late for school.
> They **aren't often** in bed before 10 p.m.

With *always* and *usually*, we need to add extra information:
> I **always** go to the cinema **on Saturdays**.
> I usually have coffee **for breakfast**.

1 Choose the correct adverbs of frequency.

Jack eats in restaurants two or three times a week.
He *often* / *never* / *always* eats in restaurants.

1 Mark and Anna go to Spain for their holidays every year.
They *usually* / *always* / *sometimes* go to Spain for their holidays.

2 Jenny doesn't like coffee. She drinks hot chocolate.
She *often* / *sometimes* / *never* drinks coffee.

3 We don't often go out on Monday evenings.
We *usually* / *never* / *always* stay at home on Monday evenings.

4 On Saturdays I go swimming, go to the shops or I stay at home.
I *sometimes* / *always* / *usually* go swimming on Saturdays.

2 Put the phrases in the correct order to make sentences.

always / my brother / on Saturdays / plays football
<u>My brother always plays football on Saturdays.</u>

1 for their holidays / Turkey / Paul and Katy / go to / usually
_____

2 before 7 p.m. / television / my parents / never / watch
_____

3 late / I am / on Monday / for class / often / mornings
_____

4 for a walk / on Sundays / sometimes / go / we
_____

5 go / don't / to the theatre / I / often
_____

6 at the weekend / to the cinema / I / go / often
_____

7 aren't / Peter and I / for classes / on time / always
_____

Anna

Hi! My name's Anna. I'm nineteen years old and I'm from a small town in Poland but now I live in Aberdeen, in Scotland. I study English at university here and it's great!

I work hard from Monday to Friday but I don't work on Friday evenings or Saturdays. On Fridays, we always go to a club or a concert. I love music and my favourite club is The Lemon Tree. On Saturdays I sometimes go shopping but usually I get up late and then I go to the park. My boyfriend always watches Aberdeen Football Club on Saturdays but I never go. I hate football!

I don't often go home to Poland but my mum often phones me. We talk for hours! I like Aberdeen but I want to live in Poland after I finish studying. Aberdeen is great but Poland is my home!

Comments (7) Gallery (20 photos)

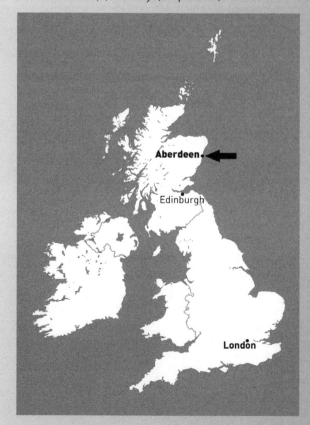

n Aberdeen

READING

1 **T6** Read and listen to the blog. What is it about?

A A Scottish girl who lives in Poland.
B A Polish girl who wants to live in Scotland.
C A Polish girl who lives in Scotland.

2 Read the text again. Are the statements true (T) or false (F)?

Anna is eighteen years old.	F
1 Anna is from Aberdeen.	☐
2 She studies English.	☐
3 She doesn't work on Saturdays.	☐
4 She never goes to clubs.	☐
5 She likes going to The Lemon Tree.	☐
6 She sometimes goes shopping on Saturdays.	☐
7 Her boyfriend likes football.	☐
8 Anna watches football with her boyfriend.	☐
9 She doesn't often go to Poland.	☐
10 Her dad often phones her.	☐
11 She wants to live in Aberdeen after she finishes her studies.	☐

SPEAKING

1 **T7** Complete the conversation with the correct forms of the verbs in the box. Then listen to check your answers.

dance eat (x2) go (x2) love not go
not like watch ~~go~~

Helen I love <u>going</u> to clubs and I always go dancing at the weekend. I like ¹_____ to the cinema but I don't like the theatre. Sometimes I watch football. I like ²_____ football, it's fun. I never eat out. I don't like ³_____ in restaurants. What about you, Lindy?

Lindy I ⁴_____ clubs because I hate ⁵_____ . I like the cinema but I ⁶_____ very often. The theatre is great. I love it. I hate football and all sports but I love restaurants. I ⁷_____ sushi once a week. I like Chinese and Italian food, too. What about you, Aleksy?

Aleksy I often ⁸_____ out but not to clubs. I hate clubs. I sometimes go to the cinema. I like films. I don't often go to the theatre but I enjoy it. I sometimes watch football with my girlfriend. She ⁹_____ football and I like it, too. I love eating Italian food.

2 **T7** Read and listen again and tick the things that the people like. What is the perfect night out for the three friends?

	Helen	Lindy	Aleksy
clubs	✓		
cinema			
theatre			
football			
eating out			

Night out: _____

3 **T8** Read about Rania and complete the sentences using the words in brackets. Listen to check your answers.

Let me tell you about what I like and don't like. I <u>don't like catching the bus</u> (not like/catch/the bus) to school. I go to school by bus every day. It leaves very early in the morning and my friends all go to school by car. I ¹_____ (not like/go to/school) at all, really. It's hard work! And I ²_____ (hate/do/exams). They're horrible!
In the evenings I often have my computer on. I ³_____ (like/play/computer games) and I send emails to friends. But my real hobby is films. I ⁴_____ (love/watch/films)! I go to the cinema every Friday with my friends.

WORD LIST

Days of the week
Monday
Tuesday
Wednesday
Thursday
Friday
Saturday
Sunday

Months
January
February
March
April
May
June
July
August
September
October
November
December

Time expressions
after (school)
always
at 8/night/the weekend
before
every (morning)
in January/the evening/the
  summer
never
often
on Monday/Sunday night
sometimes
usually

Greetings
Be my Valentine!
Best wishes
Congratulations (on …)!
Good luck (in …)!
Happy anniversary!
Lots of love
Many happy returns!
Well done (for …)!

In the town (1)
bus
café
canal
cinema
city centre
club
concert
disco
gallery
library
museum
park (n)
restaurant
shop
taxi
tram
underground
university

Other
aged
band
boat
(bon)fire
bowling
busy
cake
candle
canteen
catch (a bus/tram)
class
classmate
clean up
come

cook (v)
crowd
dance (v)
date (n)
different
do sport
drink (v)
drive (v)
driving test
early (adv)
eat
enjoy
exam
famous
finish (n, v)
fireworks
forget
free time
fun (n)
get dressed
get up
get/go home
go
go out
go to bed
hate (v)
have
have a break
have a shower
have breakfast/lunch/dinner
help (v)
home city
hot chocolate
know
late (adv, adj)
like
listen (to)
live (adj)
live (v)
lunchtime
meal
meet
midnight
mixed school
musician
noise
notebook
office
open (v)
organised
pass (v)
play
prepare
present (n)
quiet
relax
rich
ride (n)
see
shirt
shopping
singer
snack
songwriter
stay (v)
strange
study (v)
swimming
take
taxi driver
think
tired
traditional
trousers
uniform
visit
waitress
wake (up)
walk (n, v)
want
watch (v)
work (n, v)
write

18

VOCABULARY

1 Complete the sentences with the correct form of a suitable verb. The first letter of each verb is given.

Mark l<u>ives</u> in Oxford but w<u>orks</u> in London.

1 Sometimes I c_____ dinner at home and sometimes I e_____ in a restaurant.

2 Joss usually c_____ a bus to work but sometimes she w_____ u_____ late and gets a taxi.

3 At the weekends I g_____ o_____ with friends and we w_____ in the park.

4 The class s_____ at nine o'clock and f_____ at ten thirty.

5 I t_____ it's OK, but I w_____ to be sure.

6 Amy g_____ u_____ at six o'clock. She has a shower, g_____ d_____ and h_____ breakfast.

7 In the evening, I often w_____ TV or l_____ to music.

8 My dad d_____ his car to work but he h_____ driving in the city centre.

2 Match the verbs to the phrases.

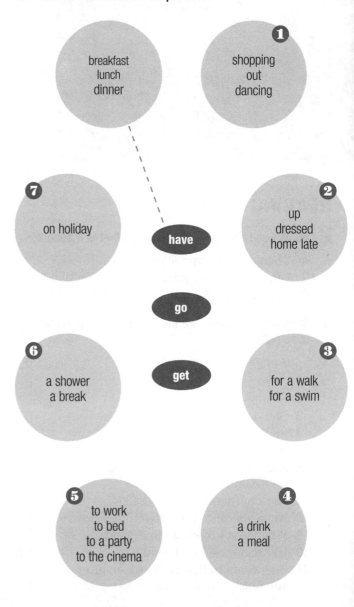

3 Write the opposites. The first letter of each word is given.

	early	late
1	come	g_____
2	winter	s_____
3	always	n_____
4	start	f_____
5	love	h_____
6	go to bed	g_____ u_____
7	after	b_____

4 Match the places in the box with the sentences.

café   cinema   ~~disco~~   gallery   library   park
restaurant   shop   university

We dance here. <u>disco</u>

1 We go for a walk here. _____
2 My sister studies here. _____
3 My parents often look at paintings here. _____
4 This is a good place to eat. _____
5 I get books from here. _____
6 I often buy things here. _____
7 My friends meet for a drink here. _____
8 We watch films here. _____

5 Complete the gaps with *in*, *at* or *on*.

<u>at</u> six o'clock

1 _____ 10:30 p.m.
2 _____ the morning
3 _____ the afternoon
4 _____ the evening
5 _____ night
6 _____ Monday
7 _____ Saturday
8 _____ the weekend
9 _____ 21 December
10 _____ Christmas Day
11 _____ your birthday
12 _____ August
13 _____ December
14 _____ 2006

6 Write the next word in the sequence.

January / February / <u>March</u>

1 breakfast / lunch / _____
2 Friday / Saturday / _____
3 November / October / _____
4 in the afternoon / in the evening / _____
5 never / sometimes / _____

WRITING | Greetings cards

1 Match the messages from greetings cards with the pictures.

1 Happy birthday! Many happy returns! ☐
2 Congratulations on your wedding! ☐
3 Congratulations on your new baby boy! ☐
4 Congratulations on passing your driving test. Well done! ☐
5 Good luck in your exam! ☐

2 Complete the greetings cards with the words from the box. Use capital letters where necessary. There are two words that you don't need.

anniversary   best   returns   congratulations
~~dear~~   luck   many   well   lots

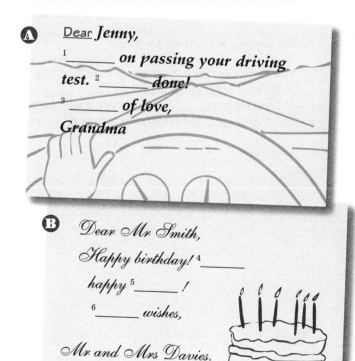

A
<u>Dear</u> *Jenny,*
¹_____ *on passing your driving test.* ²_____ *done!*
³_____ *of love,*
Grandma

B
Dear Mr Smith,
Happy birthday! ⁴_____
happy ⁵_____ !
⁶_____ *wishes,*
Mr and Mrs Davies.

VOCABULARY AND GRAMMAR

1 Complete the text. Use the correct forms of the words in capital letters. (5 points)

My name's Silvio. I'm from Rome.
I'm <u>Italian</u>. My mother's from Madrid.   ITALY
She's ¹_____ . I'm a student   SPAIN
in London. My teacher's name is
Stephanie. She isn't ²_____ .   ENGLAND
She's from Budapest. She's
³_____ . The other students   HUNGARY
in my class are from France, Italy
and Spain and there are
⁴_____ and   JAPAN
⁵_____ students. It's great!   EGYPT

2 Complete the sentences with the names of family members. (6 points)

Your mother and father are your <u>parents</u>.

1 Your uncle's son is your _____ .
2 Your sister's daughter is your _____ .
3 Your brother's son is your _____ .
4 Your uncle's wife is your _____ .
5 Your mother's second husband is your

_____ .

6 Your father's mother is your _____ .

3 Complete the text. Write one word in each gap. (8 points)

My name's Paula. I <u>am</u> a student at a language school in London. I live with a girl from Italy. ¹_____ name is Gina. We ²_____ always late for school! I get up ³_____ 7 o'clock and ⁴_____ dressed but Gina loves sleeping and she gets up very late. Our teacher is an English man. ⁵_____ name is Dan. He ⁶_____ a very good teacher. ⁷_____ the afternoon we often go for a walk. ⁸_____ Saturdays we go to a club and relax.

4 Complete the questions. (4 points)

What<u>'s her name</u>?
Her name is Paula.

1 Where _____ ?
Gina is from Italy.
2 What time _____ ?
Paula gets up at 7 o'clock.
3 What _____ ?
Their teacher's name is Dan.
4 Where _____ ?
At weekends they go to a club.

5 Complete the sentences with the correct forms of the verbs in brackets. (3 points)

Jo <u>doesn't walk</u> (not walk) to school. She always <u>catches</u> (catch) a bus.

1 We _____ (not work) at a university.
We _____ (work) at a school.
2 He _____ (not be) American. He lives in Boston but he _____ (not come) from Boston.
3 My sister _____ (study) a lot. She _____ (not get) home before 9 p.m.

6 Choose the correct words or phrases. (4 points)

My (brother's)/ brothers house is very big.

1 My *friend's / friends* like playing computer games.
2 My *parent's / parents'* names are Bob and Carol.
3 They *are always / always are* happy at Christmas.
4 I *often go / go often* for a walk with my friends.
5 We are students. *Their / Our* names are Mark and Paul.
6 My brother is married. *He's / His* wife's name is Belinda.
7 My birthday is *in / on* January.
8 I don't like *getting / get* up early in the morning.

LISTENING SKILLS

7 [T9] Listen to Martin talking to his friend Jose about his family. Are the statements true (T) or false (F)?

(7 points)

1 Martin is in Germany now. ☐
2 Martin comes from Bonn. ☐
3 They get up at 6 o'clock in the morning. ☐
4 School in England and Germany starts at 8. ☐
5 They don't always have breakfast at home. ☐
6 They always go for a walk at the weekend. ☐
7 They sometimes go to the cinema. ☐

READING SKILLS

8 Read the text and choose the correct answers.

(6 points)

1 Before they go on holiday, Amy and her friends
   a have an early night.
   b sleep at the same place.
   c wake up at the same time.
   d stay up all night.

2 Amy hates
   a getting up early to go on holiday.
   b getting ready for holidays.
   c waiting to go on holiday.
   d the night before a holiday.

3 They start at
   a 5 a.m.
   b 8 a.m.
   c 5 p.m.
   d a different time each year.

4 She enjoys
   a watching the people in the street.
   b seeing lots of cars.
   c eating breakfast before she sets off.
   d seeing nothing in the street.

5 At 8 o'clock they
   a finish their drive.
   b always go for a walk.
   c have a short break.
   d sleep in the car.

6 What does Amy NOT do on holiday?
   a have barbecues
   b go swimming
   c get up early
   d eat much.

COMMUNICATION

9 Put the phone conversation in the correct order.

(7 points)

a Is Jenny there? ☐
b Fine thanks. And you? ☐
c Good afternoon. Chester 5154767. ☐ 1
d Goodbye Mrs Green. Hi, Jenny. ☐
e Yes, hold on a minute. Jenny, it's Will. Goodbye, Will. ☐
f Hello, Will. How are you? ☐
g Very well, thank you, Will. ☐
h Hello, Mrs Green. It's Will here. ☐

Total ☐ /50

YOUR FAVOURITES • YOUR FAVOURITES • YOUR FAVOURITES

Getting ready for holidays

This week in our series 'Your favourites' Amy Rogers talks about her favourite day.

"What's my favourite day? I love going on holiday. I love getting ready, making food and putting clothes in bags. I always go on holiday with Claire, Terry and Steve, my friends from school. They stay at my house the night before we go on holiday. We talk and watch a video and always go to bed late. I never sleep and I always wake my friends up in the morning. I hate waiting to go. Terry and Steve always drink coffee and sometimes have breakfast before we go. I put the bags in the car and then we go. I never eat or drink before we go. We always leave at 5 o'clock. It's very early in the morning and I love driving in the quiet streets. All the lights are off and the people are asleep. At 8 o'clock, we usually stop for a rest. On sunny days, we go for a walk and, when the weather is bad, we sit in the car and eat and drink. In the afternoon, the roads are full of cars. I hate sitting in the car not moving. We usually get to our holiday house at 5 o'clock in the afternoon. It's a small house near the beach. I love it. I love swimming in the sea and having barbecues on the beach. I love eating a lot and getting up late. The only thing I don't like is coming home again!"

21

 # Looks good

GRAMMAR

have got

	Affirmative	Negative
I/You/We/They	have got ('ve got) a phone.	have not got (haven't got) a phone.
He/She/It	has got ('s got) a phone.	has not got (hasn't got) a phone.

We use *have got* to talk about:
- possessions: *I've got a new car.*
  My mobile phone's got a camera.
- people in your life: *I've got two brothers and one sister.*
- physical characteristics: *I've got blue eyes.*
- illnesses: *I've got a headache.*

Yes/No questions			Short answers
Have	I/you/we/they	got a phone?	Yes, I/you/we/they **have**. No, I/you/we/they **haven't**.
Has	he/she/it		Yes, he/she/it **has**. No, he/she/it **hasn't**.

Wh- questions
What have you got in your bag?
How many books have you got?

> ### Mind the trap!
> *I'm eighteen.* (NOT ~~I've got eighteen.~~)
> *I'm hungry.* (NOT ~~I've got hunger.~~)

1 Complete the sentences with the correct form of *have got*: affirmative (+) or negative (–).

He <u>has got</u> a red bag. (+)
1 We _____ our pens and pencils. (+)
2 I _____ a comb. (–)
3 Has she got an ID card? No, she _____ . (–)
4 Have you got a mobile phone?
   Yes, I _____ . (+)
5 This flat _____ a bedroom. (–)
6 They _____ any water. (–)

2 What have they got in their bags? Look at the table and write sentences.

	Wallet	Comb	MP3 player
Joe	✗	✓	✓
Lizzie	✓	✗	✓
Andy	✓	✓	✗
Angie and Sam	✗	✓	✓

(+) Joe<u>'s got a comb and an MP3 player.</u>
(–) He <u>hasn't got a wallet.</u>
1 (+) Lizzie _____ .
   (–) She _____ .
2 (+) Andy _____ .
   (–) He _____ .
3 (+) Angie and Sam _____ .
   (–) They _____ .

3 Look at the table in Exercise 2. Complete the questions and short answers.

Joe / a wallet in his bag?
<u>Has Joe got a wallet in his bag?</u>
<u>No, he hasn't.</u>
1 Lizzie / a comb in her bag?
   _____
   _____
2 Angie and Sam / an MP3 player in their bag?
   _____
   _____
3 Angie and Sam / wallet in their bag?
   _____
   _____

4 Choose the correct phrases.

I always ⟨have⟩ / *have got* coffee for breakfast.
1 *Have you* / *Have you got* a dictionary?
2 At weekends we sometimes *have* / *have got* lunch in the garden.
3 He *hasn't got* / *haven't got* his mobile phone with him – it's at home.
4 My mobile phone *have got* / *has got* a video camera and an MP3 player.
5 *Do you have* / *Have you got* tea or coffee for breakfast?
6 She *is* / *has got* fifteen years old.
7 We *don't have* / *haven't got* lunch at home.
8 How many pens *has he* / *he has* got?

SPEAKING

1 🔊T10 **Complete the description of Roza with** *has got* **or** *is*. **Then listen to check your answers.**

Roza is Hungarian.
She ¹_____ 1.66 m tall.
She ²_____ long hair.
She ³_____ brown eyes.
She ⁴_____ about
twenty years old.
She ⁵_____ very
good-looking.

2 🔊T11 **Choose the correct answer. Then listen and check.**

My favourite musician is Beyoncé.
a I like Beyoncé.
b I'm like Beyoncé.
c I look like Beyoncé.

1 My dad and I are both shy.
a I like my dad.
b I'm like my dad.
c I look like my dad.

2 My mum and I are both tall with fair, curly hair and brown eyes.
a I like my mum.
b I'm like my mum.
c I look like my mum.

3 Rashid is very easy-going, and his brother, Ali, is the same.
a Ali likes Rashid.
b Ali is like Rashid.
c Ali looks like Rashid.

4 My big sister thinks Jay-Z is great.
a She likes Jay-Z.
b She is like Jay-Z.
c She looks like Jay-Z.

5 Look at this photo of my friend, Jim.
a He likes David Beckham.
b He is like David Beckham.
c He looks like David Beckham.

3 🔊T12 **Choose the correct phrases. Then listen and check.**

A Matt's exactly like Tim. They're like identical twins.
B No, they aren't.
A Yes, they are. *They are both* / *They both are* tall and ¹ *they have both got* / *they both have got* brown eyes.
B Yes, but…
A ² *They both like* / *They like both* rock music and ³ *they play both* / *they both play* the guitar.
B Yes, but…
A And they ⁴ *are both* / *have both got* good at tennis and they ⁵ *are both* / *have both got* lively and confident.
B Yes, but Matt's twenty and Tim's thirty-five… and Tim's Chinese!
A Yes, but, apart from that…

4 🔊T13 **Complete the description with words from the box. Then listen and check.**

are both	good at	has got	have both got
~~is~~	is like	likes	looks like

Shannon is seventeen years old. She ¹_____ long, blonde hair. She ²_____ her mum. They ³_____ blue eyes and long hair. They ⁴_____ very good-looking. Shannon ⁵_____ very easy-going. She is ⁶_____ her dad. He is very easy-going, too. Shannon ⁷_____ music and she's very ⁸_____ singing.

GRAMMAR

Possessive pronouns

We use possessive adjectives with nouns:
*This is **my** house.*
We use possessive pronouns to replace nouns: *It's **mine**.*

Possessive adjectives	Possessive pronouns
This is **my** room.	It's **mine**.
This is **your** room.	It's **yours**.
This is **his** room.	It's **his**.
This is **her** room.	It's **hers**.
This is **our** room.	It's **ours**.
This is **their** room	It's **theirs**.

Mind the trap!

There is no possessive pronoun for the possessive adjective *its*.

This is my dog and this is its bed.
(NOT ~~This is my dog and this bed is its.~~)

1 Complete the second sentence so that it has the same meaning as the first sentence. Use possessive adjectives and possessive pronouns.

> This is my book.
> This book is <u>mine</u>.

1 That isn't his calculator.
That calculator isn't _____ .

2 Is this purse yours?
Is this _____ purse?

3 Those aren't my textbooks.
Those textbooks aren't _____ .

4 These cups are ours.
These are _____ cups.

5 Are those her sandwiches?
Are those sandwiches _____ ?

2 Look at the table and complete the sentences with possessive adjectives and possessive pronouns.

	me	my brother	my sister	my cousins
trainers	black	white	old	
school		big		small
hair	straight	dark	curly	

My brother and I have got new trainers. <u>His</u> are white and ¹_____ are black. My sister hasn't got new trainers. ²_____ are old. We don't go to the same school as our cousins. ³_____ school is big but ⁴_____ is small. Me and my sister have both got blonde hair. ⁵_____ hair is curly but ⁶_____ is straight. My brother looks different – ⁷_____ hair is dark.

LISTENING

1 〔T14〕 Listen and match the names with the photos.

Bruce   Emma   Phillip   Katy

1 _____   2 _____

3 _____   4 _____

2 〔T14〕 Listen again. Are the statements true (T), false (F) or is there no information (NI)?

1 Katy's twenty-five. ☐
2 Katy isn't good at sports. ☐
3 Bruce has got curly hair. ☐
4 Bruce has green eyes. ☐
5 Philip's eyes are blue. ☐
6 Philip's hard-working. ☐
7 Emma is tall. ☐
8 Emma's sixteen. ☐

3 〔T15〕 Listen to the descriptions and answer the questions.

Description 1
What colour eyes has he got?
<u>brown</u>
1 What does he like?
_____

Description 2
2 What colour eyes has she got?
_____
3 What is she good at?
_____

Description 3
4 Do the two girls look similar?
_____
5 What colour hair has the speaker got?
_____

READING

1 Match the words with the pictures.

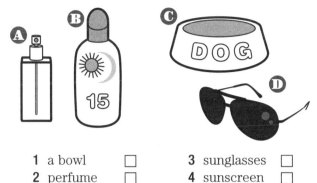

1 a bowl ☐   3 sunglasses ☐
2 perfume ☐   4 sunscreen ☐

2 **T16** Read and listen to the introduction to an article on dogs. Complete the sentences with numbers.

1 In America, people spend _____ a year on their pets.
2 _____ percent of American dogs get presents at Christmas.
3 The writer gives _____ differences between dogs and children.

3 **T17** Read and listen to the second part of the text and complete the sentences with one or two words.

Alette's owner's name is Sophie.

1 Alette lives in _____ .
2 Alette wears Chien 56 _____ .
3 The weather in Sydney is hot and _____ .
4 Marcus looks great in _____ .
5 Squidgie's got a lot of _____ .
6 Every week, Heidi buys Squidgie _____ .

4 Read the article again and match the sentences with the dogs. Use A for Alette, M for Marcus or S for Squidgie.

This dog wears perfume. ☐A

1 This dog wears sunscreen. ☐
2 This dog eats from a Gucci bowl. ☐
3 This dog has got a Louis Vuitton bag. ☐
4 This dog wears sunglasses. ☐
5 This dog has got a lot of clothes. ☐

I love my dog

Worldwide, we spend fifty billion US dollars a year on pets (thirty-five billion of this in the USA), mainly on cats and dogs. Sixty percent of US dogs now get Christmas presents. 'Dogs are the new children,' says John Ryan of *The New York Dog Magazine*. But dogs are not exactly like children. They don't ask for money, take the car or stay out late. Here are some lucky dogs…

GLOSSARY
1 billion = 1,000,000,000

Alette lives in the centre of Paris, France. She eats from a Gucci bowl. She's got a Louis Vuitton bag. She wears Chien 56 perfume. Yes, Alette is a very lucky dog. Her owner Sophie Lambert says, 'I love my dog and I want her to be happy.'

Marcus lives in Sydney, Australia. Sydney is hot and sunny, but that's no problem for Marcus. He wears Doggles sunglasses and sunscreen. His owner is Mike Offbach. Mike says, 'Marcus has problems in the sun. These products are great, and he looks great in the sunglasses.'

You can love your dog in cold countries, too. Squidgie lives in Oslo, Norway, with his owner Heidi Reidarson. Squidgie has got lots of clothes, including coats, sweaters, shorts, shoes and hats. Heidi says, 'Squidgie is a pet, but he's my friend, too. I buy him new things every week. I've got the money, so why not?'

WORD LIST

Possessions
bag
bottle of water
calculator
comb
ID card
MP3 player
notebook
pen
pencil
(mobile) phone
purse
textbook
trainers
wallet

Appearance

Eyes
blue
(light) brown
green
soft

Hair
bald
black
blonde
curly
dark (adj)
fair
grey
long
medium-length
short
straight
wavy

Face
round

Age
middle-aged
old
young

Size
fat (adj)
short
slim
small
tall
thin

Opinion
attractive
beautiful
good-looking
pretty
ugly

Personality
character
confident
easy-going
energetic
friendly
hard-working
intelligent
kind (adj)
lazy
lively
nervous

quiet
relaxed
serious
shy

Other
a bit
(a lot) in common
again
animal
basketball
be allowed to
bedroom
both
car
cat
choose
computer
cup
department
dictionary
dirty
each
ear
envelope
exactly
exam paper
film (n)
flatmate
good at
graduation
happy
have got
hers
his
horrible
housewarming
keep fit
kind (n)
length
look (v)
look like each other
loud
mate
mine (pron)
nose
ours
outside
owner
pet
practise
ring (v)
room
sandwich
similar
sleep (v)
smoke (v)
sports centre
sure
surprised
talk
tennis
theirs
together
type (n)
ugly
wash (v)
weekday
winter
worried
yours

VOCABULARY

1 Label the picture.

face _____

2 _____

3 _____

1 _____

4 _____

2 Complete the sentences using the adjectives in brackets in the correct order.

Anna's got <u>long</u>, <u>dark</u> hair. (long, dark)

1 John's a _____ , _____ , _____ man.
(good-looking, tall, middle-aged)
2 Pete's a _____ , _____ man. (bald, short)
3 Andrea's got _____ , _____ , _____ hair.
(wavy, dark, short)
4 Minnie's got _____ , _____ eyes. (beautiful, green)
5 I've got a _____ , _____ , _____ mobile phone. (new, great, small)

3 Complete the sentences with one word. The first letter of each word is given.

Tom's eyes are the same colour as hot chocolate! They're b<u>rown</u>.

1 He hasn't got any hair. He's b_____ .
2 She's about fifty. She's m_____-a _____ .
3 My dad is 1.40 m tall. He's s_____ .
4 Your dog isn't attractive at all! It's u_____.
5 Her hair isn't long and it isn't short.
It's m_____-l_____ .
6 I don't know if his hair is black or brown but it's not blonde. It's d_____ .
7 Natalia's hair isn't straight and it isn't curly.
It's w_____ .

4 Complete the sentences with words from the box.

allowed bit ~~common~~ good like look
pets sure

We have a lot in <u>common</u>.

1 I'm a _____ shy.
2 Do you _____ like your dad?
3 Are you _____ to use your brother's computer?
4 What is your flatmate _____ ?
5 We've got five _____, three dogs and two cats.
6 I'm _____ this is my pen.
7 What sports are you _____ at?

5 Label the pictures.

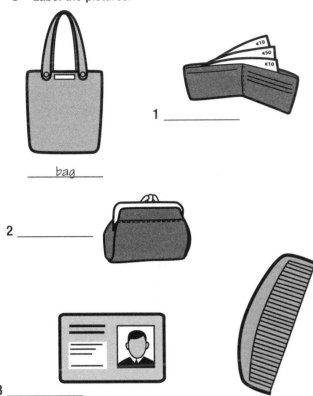

_____bag_____

1 _____

2 _____

3 _____

4 _____

6 Complete the words with one letter in each gap.

three electronic devices:

c <u>a</u> l <u>c</u> u <u>l</u> <u>a</u> t o <u>r</u>

1 m __ __ __l __ p __ __n __

2 c __ __ p __ __ __r

two things to read:

3 t __ __ t __ __ __k

4 d __ __ t __ __ n __ r __

two sports:

5 b __ __ k __ __ b __ __ __

6 t __ __ n __ __

something to eat:

7 s __ __ d __ __ c __

a type of party:

8 h __ __ s __ w __ __ m __ __ __

7 Choose the odd one out.

fat, slim, ~~curly~~, small

1 short, slim, energetic, thin
2 wavy, straight, grey, middle-aged
3 confident, round, relaxed, lazy
4 brown, middle-aged, old, young

WRITING | Linking words

1 Complete the sentences with *and*, *so*, *but* and *because*.

She's clever <u>and</u> attractive.

1 He's clever _____ lazy.
2 I play tennis a lot _____ I like it.
3 I want to speak good English _____ I practise a lot.
4 I enjoy listening to music _____ I'm not a musician.
5 I love Indian food _____ Chinese food.
6 I haven't got my bag _____ it's in my dad's car.
7 I don't like dancing or loud music _____ I never go to nightclubs.

2 Put the email in the correct order.

New GF

Reply   Reply All   Forward   Follow Up

From: lou.cafiso@xyz.com
To: andy.mcintyre@yes.com
Subject: New GF

Hi Andy,
I've got a new girlfriend!

a blue eyes. She loves tennis so ☐
b really good at tennis, but ☐
c Her name's Lana. She's tall and ☐ 1
d he's not very clever. I play ☐
e I don't play with Lana because ☐
f with Lana's friend, Jo. She's nice but ☐
g now I play every evening – but ☐
h I'm not very good at tennis. She ☐
i very attractive. She's got long hair and ☐
j she's very shy so we don't talk much. ☐
k plays with the tennis teacher. He's ☐

Write soon!
All the best,
Lou

04 Work

GRAMMAR

have to

	Affirmative	Negative
I/You/We/They	**have to** get up early.	**don't have to** get up early.
He/She/It	**has to** get up early.	**doesn't have to** get up early.

Yes/No questions				Short answers
Do	I/you/we/they	**have to** get up early?		Yes, I/we/you/they **do**. No, I/we/you/they **don't**.
Does	he/she/it			Yes, he/she/it **does**. No, he/she/it **doesn't**.

It's necessary: *Jim's a pilot. He* **has to** *wear a uniform.*

It isn't necessary: *Lorraine's a teacher. She* **doesn't have to** *wear a uniform.*

Wh- questions
What do I have to wear?
When do you have to start work?
Where does he have to go?
Who do you have to email?
How many hours does she have to work?
Which books do we have to read?

1 Complete the sentences with the correct form of *have to*: affirmative (+) or negative (–).

We <u>have to</u> get up at 6 a.m. (+)

1 He _____ wear a uniform. (+)
2 She _____ have any special qualifications. (–)
3 You _____ work on Saturdays. (–)
4 They _____ do the washing up. (+)
5 I _____ help my mum in the kitchen. (–)

2 Put the words in the correct order to make questions. Then match them to the answers.

get up early? / you / to / Do / have
<u>Do you have to get up early?</u>   A

1 have / to / your mum / work at night? / Does
_____ ☐

2 do / What time / have / go home? / to / you
_____ ☐

3 Does / have / your brother / to / wash up?
_____ ☐

4 to / have / wear a uniform? / Do / policemen
_____ ☐

5 to / you and your friends / Do / at the weekend? / have / do homework
_____ ☐

6 have / have / What qualifications / do / to / for this job? / you
_____ ☐

A ~~Yes, I do.~~   E No, we don't.
B None, anyone can do it.   F No, he doesn't.
C Yes, they do.   G At ten o'clock.
D Yes, she does.

3 Complete Tom's questions using the phrases in brackets and the correct form of *have to*.

Tom Hi, Lena. Do you like your new job?
Lena Oh, hi! Yes, it's great. I work with Beth at the holiday camp.
Tom <u>Do you have to work hard?</u> (you/work hard)
Lena Yes, we do.
Tom ¹_____ ? (How many hours/you/work every day)
Lena About ten.
Tom ²_____ ? (you/wear a uniform)
Lena I don't, but Beth does.
Tom ³_____ ? (What/she/wear)
Lena She has to wear a red uniform. It's awful.
Tom I'd like to work with you.
⁴_____ ? (I/have/special qualifications)
Lena For some jobs you do, but not for babysitting.
Tom Babysitting! ⁵_____ ? (What/a babysitter/do)
Lena Look after the children in the evening. It's great fun!
Tom ⁶_____ ? (babysitters/work long hours)
Lena No. Well, they have to wait for the parents to come back.
Tom Hmm. ⁷_____ ? (Who/I/talk to about the job)
Lena Me. I'm the babysitters' boss! You have to do what I tell you!

READING

1 Look at the pictures. Which person:

1 has to be good at swimming? ☐
2 has to wear a uniform? ☐
3 has to be good with children? ☐

2 **T18** Read and listen to the article. Write the jobs from Exercise 1 in the spaces.

A babysitter

B lifeguard

C waitress

SUMMER JOBS

At the Beach Side Holiday Camp

1 ....

Get the job

You have to be at least sixteen years old. You have to be hard-working, friendly and energetic. You have to speak good English.

Do the job

Our restaurants are open from **11 a.m.** to **3 p.m.** and from **6 p.m.** to midnight every day. You have to be here at **10 a.m.** so it's a long day. You have to wear a uniform but you don't have to wash it – we do that for you!

2 ....

Get the job

You have to be over eighteen years old and very good with children. You don't have to have any special qualifications but you need to understand and like children.

Do the job

You have to work in the evenings from 6 p.m. until midnight from Tuesday to Sunday. You don't have to work alone – we have got a special 'evening room' for children to go to and there are five people to look after them. You don't have to wear a uniform but you have to look nice.

3 ....

Get the job

You have to be at least eighteen years old. You have to be strong, a good swimmer and you have to have special qualifications in life-saving.

Do the job

Your job is to save people's lives. So you have to be ready to act quickly at any time. You have to work between 9 a.m. and 5 p.m. every day.

3 Read the article again. Are the statements true (T) or false (F)?

Lifeguards have to be at least eighteen years old. ☐T☐

1 Waiters have to speak French. ☐
2 Babysitters have to work in the morning. ☐
3 Babysitters don't have to wear a uniform. ☐
4 Lifeguards have to work at night. ☐
5 Waiters don't have to wash their uniforms. ☐
6 Lifeguards have to have special qualifications. ☐
7 Waiters have to be friendly. ☐
8 Babysitters have to work alone. ☐
9 All the people have to work at the weekend. ☐

4 Answer the questions.

Dan wants to be a lifeguard. Does he have to be eighteen?
Yes, he does.

1 James wants to be a lifeguard. Does he have to work at night?
_____

2 We want to be waitresses. Do we have to work hard?
_____

3 Lisa and Ruth want to be babysitters. Do they have to have special qualifications?
_____

29

GRAMMAR

can / can't for ability

Affirmative	Negative
I/You/He/She/It/We/They **can** swim.	I/You/He/She/It/We/They **can't** swim.

Questions	Short answers
Can I/you/he/she/it/we/they swim?	Yes, I/you/he/she/it/we/they **can**.
	No, I/you/he/she/it/we/they **can't**.

Wh- questions:
How many languages can you speak?
What meals can you cook?
Which of these instruments can you play?

Object pronouns

Object pronouns are used as objects in a sentence.

Subject	Verb	Object
I	like	**her**.
She	likes	**me**.
We	like	**them**.

Subject pronouns	Object pronouns
I	**me**
you	**you**
he	**him**
she	**her**
it	**it**
we	**us**
they	**them**

---

1 Look at the table and complete the email with *can* or *can't*.

Nova Scotia Summer Camp
International Summer Programme: Group 1

	dance	play the guitar	ride a horse	cook
Jim	✓	✓		
Jan	✓		✓	
Anna		✓	✓	
Etta		✓		✓
Marc	✓		✓	

NEW MESSAGE ☒

From: jim@world.coo
To: Matt White
Subject: Hi!

Hi Matt,

I am at a summer camp here in Scotland! I am in a group with Anna and Jan. We <u>can</u> all do very different things! Jan ¹_____ dance, and Anna ²_____ play the guitar. They ³_____ both ride a horse, too. Anna ⁴_____ dance, but it is OK, because she doesn't like going out. The only problem is that we ⁵_____ cook! We have to find someone who ⁶_____ ! ☺

Take care,

Jim

2 Look at the table in Exercise 1 again. Write sentences about what the people *can* and *can't* do.

Anna <u>can play the guitar and she can ride a horse.</u>
She <u>can't dance and she can't cook.</u>

1 Etta _____ .
  She _____ .
2 Marc _____ .
  He _____ .
3 Marc and Anna _____ .
  They _____ .
4 Etta and Jim _____ .
  They _____ .

3 Look at the table in Exercise 1 again. Write the questions and short answers.

Anna / dance
<u>Can Anna dance?</u>
<u>No, she can't.</u>

1 Etta / dance

_____

_____

2 Marc / ride a horse

_____

_____

3 Anna and Jim / play the guitar

_____

_____

4 Marc and Jan / cook

_____

_____

4 Complete the texts with subject and object pronouns from the boxes. You can use some of the words more than once.

| I | me | he | him |

My friend Joe is good at English and _I_ 'm not, so ¹_____ helps ²_____ with my English homework. But ³_____ 's not good at Maths, so ⁴_____ help ⁵_____ with his Maths homework.

| us | they | them |

My aunt and uncle have a house at the beach and we stay with ⁶_____ for two weeks every summer. When my aunt and uncle come to the city, ⁷_____ always stay with ⁸_____ in our apartment.

| him | she | her |

Cindy is Paul's girlfriend. He loves ⁹_____ and ¹⁰_____ loves ¹¹_____ , but his parents don't like ¹²_____ because ¹³_____ isn't very easy-going.

SPEAKING

1 〔T19〕 **Match the requests with the answers. Then listen and check.**

Mum, can Mark borrow this DVD? ☑ C

1 Can we go to the cinema tonight? ☐

2 Can I give you my homework tomorrow? ☐

3 Miss James, can Jane sit with me today? ☐

4 Could we open the window, please? ☐

A No, I'm sorry. You have to do it today.

B I'm afraid not. You always talk when you sit together.

C ~~Yes, of course. Tell him it's no problem.~~

D No, I'm sorry. It's very noisy outside.

E Yes, that's fine. Just do your homework first.

2 **Write questions to ask for permission. Use *can* or *could*.**

I want to use your mobile phone.
Can/Could I use your mobile phone, please?

1 I want to use the bathroom.
_____ , please?

2 I want to leave class early.
_____ , please?

3 I want to borrow a pen.
_____ , please?

4 We want to leave our bags in the hotel.
_____ , please?

5 We want to sit here.
_____ , please?

3 〔T20〕 **Write the conversations. Use the words in the boxes and the pictures to help you. Then listen and check.**

| are | borrow | Could I | course | Here | of |
| Yes | you | your | pen |

A _Could I borrow your pen?_
B _Yes, of course. Here you are._

❶

| afraid | car | Could I | I'm | I | it | need |
| not | use | your | please |

A _____
B _____

❷

| Can I | my mum | mobile phone | no |
| that's fine | on | call | problem | Yes | your |

A _____
B _____

WORD LIST

Activities and hobbies
acting
cooking
craft
dancing
football
horse-riding/ride a horse
play the piano/the guitar
riding a bike
swimming
theatre

Jobs
artist
author
babysitter
builder
bus driver
cake decorator
chef
chocolate maker
computer programmer
cook (n)
doctor
engineer
farmer
firefighter
gardener
ice cream tester
nurse
pilot
police officer
postman/postwoman
referee
shop assistant
taxi driver
teacher
university professor
vet
window cleaner

Work
be good with
boss
earn
money
passion
pay (v)
skills
special qualifications/
    equipment
unemployed
voluntary work
wear special clothes/
    a uniform/boots
well-paid
work hard
work long hours

Other
a lot
ambitious
application form
bar
be afraid (of sth)
be asleep
be no good (at)
boring
borrow
break (v)
buy (v)
clever
cold

college
company
cool
current
date of birth
difficult
driving licence
during
easy
education
email (v)
employment
everywhere
experience
extra
fashionable
fast (adv)
female
find
future (n)
get sth ready (for)
give
hat
have fun
have to
help (n)
hot
hotel
important
interesting
Internet
lemon
look after
love (n)
male
nationality
necessary
need (v)
noisy
own (adj)
perfect
primary school
quickly (adv)
railway line
run (v)
seat (n)
sell (v)
seller
sex
sing
sit
slowly
somebody else
someone/somebody
something
spend (time/money)
start (v)
story
summer camp
sushi
swim (v)
swimmer
table
teach
temperature
ticket
tournament
understand
vanilla
visitor
wash up
weather
well (adv)
without

32

VOCABULARY

1 Write the jobs.

This person:
writes books a u t h o r

1 looks after children

— — — — — — — —

2 prepares food __ __ __ __
3 wears a uniform, has a dangerous job

— — — —
— — — — — — — —

4 works in the garden

— — — — — — —

5 wears a uniform, works in a hospital

— — — — —

6 wears a uniform, flies aeroplanes

— — — — —

7 brings your letters

— — — — — — —
or __ __ __ __ __ __ __ __ __

8 works in a shop __ __ __ __

— — — — — — — —

9 drives a car __ __ __ __

— — — — — —

10 is a doctor for animals __ __ __
11 cleans windows __ __ __ __ __ __

— — — — — — —

2 Are these words adjectives, nouns, adverbs or verbs? Choose the odd one out.

future, story, education, sell   sell

1 earn, fast, swim, start   _____
2 interesting, cold, dancing, boring   _____
3 quickly, break, slowly, well   _____
4 voluntary, pilot, nurse, teacher   _____

3 Complete the sentences using one word from each box.

application	date of	driving	long	primary
somebody	special	~~summer~~	voluntary	

~~camp~~	birth	school	work	licence	form
hours	qualifications	else			

My brother goes to a summer camp for two weeks every July.

1 Do you need _____ for this job?
2 My dad works very _____ – sometimes he gets home at 10 p.m.
3 I haven't got a _____ so I have to go to work by bus.
4 I haven't got a job but I do _____ at my local hospital.
5 We have to find _____ to work in the shop.
6 'What is your _____ ?' '16/05/1994.'
7 Could you complete this _____ , please?
8 My son goes to a very good _____ . He loves his teacher.

4 Match the activities to the pictures.

acting   cooking   dancing   playing football
playing the piano   riding a bike
riding a horse   ~~swimming~~

swimming

1 _____

3 _____

4 _____

5 _____

6 _____

7 _____

5 Complete the sentences with one word.

I'm not good <u>at</u> dancing.

1 Are you good _____ children?
2 What are you afraid _____ ?
3 I have to get the restaurant tables ready _____ dinner.
4 Can you look _____ my bag, please?
5 I hate washing _____

WRITING | Application forms

1 Read the description and complete the application form for Tom Doffman.

Tom Doffman is from Oxford. He's a university student but he wants to work at summer camp in the summer. He's twenty years old – his birthday is on 23 October. He isn't married. He likes sports and he's an excellent swimmer. He's interested in music and he can play the guitar. He is friendly, energetic and hard-working. He's got a driving licence and a gold medal for swimming. He wants to work from 1 to 30 August.

SUNNYFIELDS SUMMER CAMP

APPLICATION FORM

Personal details:

Job: <u>Summer school helper</u>

Dates: from [1]_____

to [2]_____

First name(s): [3]_____

Surname: [4]_____

Sex: [5]_____

Age: [6]_____

Date of birth: [7]_____ / _____ / 1991

Nationality: [8]_____

Marital status: [9]_____

Occupation: [10]_____

Interests and abilities:

[11]_____ (I'm very good at swimming)
and [12]_____ (I can play the guitar)

Qualifications:

Sports: [13]_____ for swimming
Other: [14]_____

Personality:

Describe yourself: I am [15]f_____, [16]e_____ and [17]h_____.

33

VOCABULARY AND GRAMMAR

1 Match the words with the correct definitions. (3 points)

wallet   MP3 player   purse   trainers
notebook   dictionary   ~~mobile phone~~

You use it to talk to people. _mobile phone_

1 You can write in it. _____
2 You wear them to play tennis. _____
3 You listen to music on it. _____
4 You check new words in it. _____
5 Women often keep money in it. _____
6 Men often keep money in it. _____

2 Choose the correct words. (7 points)

Tom is very _____ . He works ten hours every day.
a shy   (b) hard-working   c bald

1 My brother doesn't do any work.
He's just _____ .
a lazy   b nice   c lively

2 Jane is very _____ . She knows that she is good at school and she knows that she is good-looking.
a lazy   b quiet   c confident

3 Is this book _____ or yours?
a mine   b me   c my

4 This is my brother's room but not everything in it is _____ .
a him   b he's   c his

5 Terry doesn't like playing. He likes reading the newspaper. He's very _____ .
a hard-working   b serious   c lively

6 I like your family's car but I like _____ more.
a us   b our   c ours

7 I'm like my mum. We are never nervous. We're both _____ .
a shy   b lively   c easy-going

3 Complete the text with one word in each gap. (4 points)

My uncle is a postman and I want to be a postman too. They have ¹_____ get up early and wear a uniform ²_____ they don't have to work in an office. They go to the post office to get the letters and they take ³_____ to people's houses. My uncle hasn't ⁴_____ special qualifications and he doesn't have to be good ⁵_____ his hands. He starts work very early ⁶_____ he finishes at lunchtime. He's got a bike and he rides ⁷_____ every day. The bike is old but it's very fast and my uncle is very good ⁸_____ riding it!

4 Complete the gaps with the correct forms of _have got_, _have to_ or _can_. (6 points)

I'm a teacher. I _don't have to_ wear a uniform.

1 She's lucky. She _____ go to school today. It's Sunday.
2 I'm very good at music but I _____ dance.
3 It's not fair. My parents say I _____ come home before 11 o'clock on Saturday.
4 My girlfriend's very attractive. She _____ blonde hair and blue eyes.
5 I've got a cat but I _____ a dog.
6 My brother _____ speak three foreign languages.

5 Complete the questions and short answers. (10 points)

A _Can you_ (you/can) dance?
B Yes, _I can_.

1 A _____ (farmers/have to) work outside?
B Yes, _____ .

2 A _____ (your father/can) cook?
B No, _____ .

3 A _____ (they/have got) a car?
B No, _____ .

4 A _____ (your school/have got) a café?
B Yes, _____ .

5 A _____ (your sister/have to) work at weekends?
B No, _____ .

LISTENING SKILLS

6 **T21** Listen to the job interview. Choose the correct answers: a, b or c. *(6 points)*

1 The boy
   a wants a job as a shop assistant.
   b works as Santa Claus in a shop.
   c wants a job as Santa Claus in a shop.

2 What can the boy do well?
   a work on a computer
   b work with children
   c look after his children

3 The boy is
   a short and fat.
   b tall and fat.
   c tall and thin.

4 In this job you have to
   a work nine hours a day.
   b work every day.
   c work for a month.

5 What happens on 3 December?
   a The boy starts his holidays.
   b The boy starts at university.
   c The boy starts work.

6 The interviewer thinks the boy
   a looks like Santa Claus.
   b is good at speaking like Santa Claus.
   c is not good at speaking like Santa Claus.

COMMUNICATION

7 Complete the dialogues with the words from the box. *(6 points)*

problem   course   afraid   here   fine
sorry   could

A <u>Could</u> I open the window, please?
B Sorry, I'm ¹_____ not. It's very cold in here.

A Can I use your dictionary, please?
B Yes, of ²_____ . ³_____ you are.

A Could you help me with my homework, please?
B Yes, that's ⁴_____ . No ⁵_____ .

A Could I use your pen, please?
B No, I'm ⁶_____ . It doesn't work.

READING SKILLS

8 Read the text on pen pals. Are the statements true (T) or false (F)? *(8 points)*

1 One person has got a sister. ☐
2 Heidi can speak German and one other language. ☐
3 Heidi has got three pets. ☐
4 Stefan works very hard. ☐
5 Stefan's parents have only got one child. ☐
6 Stefan wants to go to university in Britain. ☐
7 Natasha is twenty-four years old. ☐
8 Natasha and Heidi both like sports. ☐

PEN PALS WANTED

"I'm **Heidi**. I'm a sixteen-year-old German girl. I'm good at sports and I love playing tennis. I can play the piano and I like singing. I've got a young brother, Klaus. My parents have got a shop. I sometimes work in the shop on Saturdays. I'm quite tall (1.70 m) and have got long hair. I can speak English and French. One day I want to be a vet – I love animals. I've got a horse and two dogs. I want a pen pal in Canada or America.

*I am a seventeen-year-old Polish boy. My name is **Stefan**. I am 1.82 m tall and I've got blonde hair and blue eyes. I think I am quite good-looking. I'm not very serious or hard-working. I am outgoing and friendly. I like playing the guitar. I'm in a band with my friends. I haven't got a brother or sister. My father is a musician and my mother is a nurse. I am at school – I don't like studying but I have to go to school for two more years. I don't want to go to university. I want to live in Britain and play the guitar. I want a girl pen pal in Scotland or Ireland.*

My name is **Natasha**. I'm from near Moscow in Russia. I am short (1.52 m). I've got dark hair and brown eyes. I've got one sister, Dana, and she is twenty-four years old. I am interested in sports and travelling. My favourite place is St Petersburg. I love swimming and I always go to the sea in the summer. I like school. I want to be a teacher. I'm quiet and shy but I like writing to people. I want a girl pen pal in Italy or Spain."

Total ☐ /50

35

05 My place

GRAMMAR

there is/there are + a/some/any

We use *some* and *any* with plural and uncountable nouns: *some* in affirmative sentences, *any* in negative sentences and questions.

	Affirmative	Negative
Singular	There is (there's) a/one bed.	There is not (isn't) a bed.
Plural	There are some/two beds.	There are not (aren't) any beds.

	Yes/No questions	Short answers
Singular	Is there a bed?	Yes, there is. No, there isn't.
Plural	Are there any beds?	Yes, there are. No, there aren't.

Mind the trap

We can use *a* or *one* in affirmative singular sentences, but we only use *a* in singular questions and negatives.

There's a/one chair in the kitchen.

Is there a chair in the kitchen?
(NOT ~~Is there one chair in the kitchen?~~)

There isn't a chair in the kitchen.
(NOT ~~There isn't one chair in the kitchen.~~)

---

1 Look at the picture and complete the sentences using the correct form of *there is/there are*.

There are two armchairs.
There isn't a sofa.
1 _____ a table.
2 _____ some plants.
3 _____ a DVD player.
4 _____ any DVDs.
5 _____ a television.
6 _____ a cupboard.
7 _____ any shelves.
8 _____ some books.

2 Look at the picture again. Write questions and short answers.

armchairs?
Are there any armchairs? Yes, there are.
sofa?
Is there a sofa? No, there isn't.

1 bed?
_____
_____

2 DVDs?
_____
_____

3 plants?
_____
_____

4 wardrobe?
_____
_____

5 books?
_____
_____

3 Choose the correct answers.

In my bedroom there 's / *are* a bed and there are [1] *any / some* shelves, but there [2] *isn't / aren't* a wardrobe. There's [3] *a / an* armchair in the corner and next to it there [4] *'s / are* some drawers for my clothes. There [5] *isn't / aren't* [6] *any / some* plants in my room, but [7] *there's / there are* some flowers outside my window.

READING

1 [T22] The text is part of a story. Read and listen. Match the paragraphs with the sentences a-c.

Paragraph 1 ☐
Paragraph 2 ☐
Paragraph 3 ☐

a gives extra information
b describes the room
c gives the location of the room

2 Find the building on the map. Choose A, B or C.

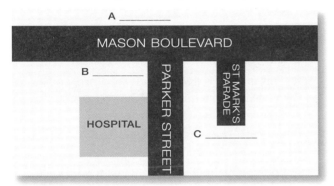

3 [T22] Listen and read again. Choose the picture which shows the room in the story.

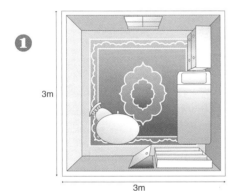

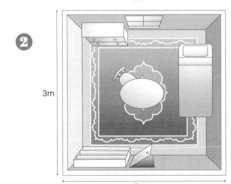

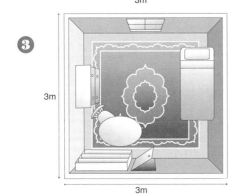

CHAPTER 3

1 The room is about three metres by three metres. There's one door and one window. The door is in the middle of a wall. The window faces the door. There's a table and a chair on the left of the door as you enter. There are some bookshelves on the right, but there aren't any books in them. There's a single bed along the wall on the right. There are some drawers next to the bed. There's an old, Turkish carpet in the middle of the room. It's a normal room.

2 The room is on the fourth floor of a building on the corner of Mason Boulevard and Parker Street next to the city hospital. It's one floor below the top floor. There's a good view of the Boulevard from the window. There are cars, shops, people. It's a normal street.

3 There's one more thing in the room. It's on the table. It's a Dragunov rifle with a telescopic sight.

4 Read the text again. Are the statements true (T) or false (F)?

There's a bed in the room. ☐T☐
1 There are some books in the room. ☐
2 The door isn't next to the window. ☐
3 The carpet is from Turkey. ☐
4 The room is on the third floor. ☐
5 The room is in a building behind the hospital. ☐
6 You can see Mason Boulevard from the room. ☐
7 There's nothing on the table. ☐

5 Choose the correct answers.

1 The window is
  a next to the door.
  b opposite the door.
  c above the door.
  d between the door and the wall.
2 There isn't a _____ in the room.
  a carpet
  b bed
  c cupboard
  d chair
3 From the window, you can't see
  a cars.
  b people.
  c shops.
  d parks.
4 There's something on
  a the table.
  b the bed.
  c the shelves.
  d the drawers.

37

GRAMMAR

Articles: *a/an*, *the*, no article

Indefinite article: *a/an*
We use *a/an* with singular nouns: ***a** mobile phone*, ***an** armchair*
We use *a* before consonant sounds: ***a** sofa*, ***a** university*
We use *an* before vowel sounds: ***an** apple*, ***an** MP3 player*

We use an indefinite article when we mention something for the first time and there are many possibilities: it's not important which one.
*Have you got **a mobile phone**?*
*I want to buy **a new computer**.*

We use an indefinite article with *There is…*
*There's **a** cat in the garden.*
*There's **an** Italian restaurant near the school.*
*Is there **a** bank near here?*

Definite article: *the*
The definite article is used with both singular and plural nouns.

We use the definite article when we mention something again after the first time and with things or groups which are unique – we know exactly which one it is.
*There's **a** table in the kitchen.*
*There's a cup on **the** table.*
*Look at **the** sky – it's beautiful.*
***The** teachers at my school are OK.*

No article
To make general statements, we use no article:
***English people** drink **tea**.*
*I like **coffee**.*
***Cats** are nice.*

1 Complete the sentences with *a, an, the* or – (no article).

The sun is 150 million kilometres away.

1 Could I have _____ glass of water, please?
2 _____ Australians love barbecues.
3 There's _____ swimming pool in the college.
4 _____ students in my class are nice.
5 I don't like _____ jazz.
6 She's _____ manager of the shop.
7 _____ cheetahs can run at 112 kilometres per hour.

a cheetah

2 Complete the conversations with *a, an, the* or – (no article).

1
A Do you like your school?
B Yes. The classrooms are great. There's ¹_____ television and ²_____ DVD player in all of them.
A Are ³_____ teachers at your school nice?
B Yes, they're cool.
A Is there ⁴_____ canteen?
B Yes, there is but I don't eat school dinners. ⁵_____ school dinners are horrible everywhere!

2
A Jim, have you got ⁶_____ pen?
B Here you are.
A This is ⁷_____ pencil.
B Oh. Hang on a minute. Here you are.
A Thanks… Hey! This is my pen.
B Oh, is it? Sorry!

3
A I don't usually like ⁸_____ fast food. Do you?
B No, I don't.
A But ⁹_____ burgers in this restaurant are fantastic.
B Mm. What's that on your chips?
A Aah! It's ¹⁰_____ spider!

4
A They've got ¹¹_____ new car.
B Again?
A Yes. That's their third new car this year.
B Where do they get ¹²_____ money to pay for it?
A I don't know. Where does he work?
B He works at ¹³_____ hospital in Green Street but he's not ¹⁴_____ doctor. He's ¹⁵_____ cleaner!

5
A What's for dinner?
B I've got something nice in ¹⁶_____ fridge. Do you like ¹⁷_____ fish?
A No, I don't. I hate ¹⁸_____ fish. Yuk!

LISTENING

1 **T23** Listen and choose the correct answers.

the newsagent's

To get to the newsagent's, ___ .
a turn right.
b turn left.
c go straight on.

1 It's on ___ .
a the right.
b the left.
c the corner.

2 It's ___ a chemist's.
a behind
b next to
c opposite

the swimming pool

3 To get to the swimming pool, take the ___ turning on the right.
a first
b second
c third

4 ___ at the lights.
a Turn right
b Turn left
c Go straight on

5 It's ___ a music shop.
a opposite
b next to
c behind

the railway station

6 To get to the railway station, ___ .
a take the first right.
b take the third right.
c go straight on.

7 Walk ___ the pub and the supermarket.
a between
b behind
c past

8 It's about ___ walk.
a five minutes'
b ten minutes'
c fifteen minutes'

2 **T24** Listen to the directions and match the places A–C to squares 1–9 on the map.
A the bank
B the supermarket
C Gallo's Pizzeria

3 You are in Gallo's Pizzeria. Your friend asks for directions to the bank. Complete the directions.

A How do I get to the bank from here?
B It's easy. Go out of the pizzeria and turn left.
Take the ¹_____ turning on the ²_____ .
Go ³_____ on to the ⁴_____ of the road and
⁵_____ left. Walk ⁶_____ the supermarket
and the car park. ⁷_____ the traffic lights turn
⁸_____ .The bank is ⁹_____ the right.

4 **T25** Listen to the directions and check your answers.

39

WORD LIST

In the town (2)
bank
bookshop
chemist's
clothes shop
concert hall
hospital
hotel
newsagent's
railway station
supermarket
theatre
traffic lights

Giving directions
across the road
corner
go/walk past sth
in front of
on your left/right
opposite
over there
straight on
take the first/second turning
    on the left/right
to the end
turn left/right (at)

House/flat and garden
armchair
basin
bath
bathroom
bed
bedroom
chair
computer
cooker
cupboard
dining room
door
drawer
DVD player
flower
fridge
furniture
hall
kitchen
knife/knives
living room
microwave
mirror
picture
plant (n)
printer
radio
shelf/shelves
shower
sink
sofa
stairs
study (n)
table
television
toilet
tree
wall
wardrobe
washing machine
window

Prepositions of place
above
behind
between
in
next to
on
under

Other
advertisement
Africa
amazing
arrive
come back
computer game
cost (v)
cosy
dream
elegant
entrance
Europe
excited
expensive
fast (adj)
fast-food restaurant
film star
fine (adj)
great
guest
high
huge
hungry
laptop
later
Latin America
map
mobile (n)
on time
open (adj)
party
place
private (adj)
remember
sad
sauna
show
single/double bed
single/double room
soon
spider
stop (v)
summer course
techno
technology
telephone (v)
terrible
today
tonight
travel (n)
view (of)
wait
walk in
warm
wonderful
word

40

VOCABULARY

1 Write the names of the rooms and complete the boxes with the contents of each room.

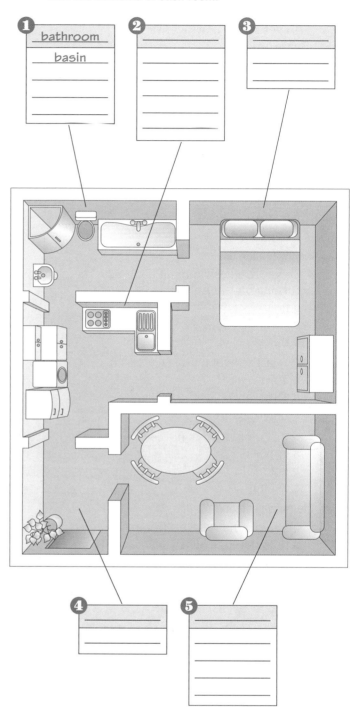

1 bathroom
basin

2 Write the places.

a place to keep money — bank

1 a place to buy aspirin _____
2 a place to stay for the night _____
3 a place to buy a newspaper _____
4 a place to see a doctor _____
5 a place to listen to music _____
6 a place to see a play _____
7 a place to buy food _____
8 a place to catch a train _____

3 Complete the sentences with one word in each gap. The first letter of each word is given.

I often d<u>ream</u> that I can fly.

1 I've got a m_____ but I don't know where I am!
2 I'm very h_____ so I want a h_____ pizza!
3 I want a room with two s_____ beds, please.
4 $20 for a burger! That's e_____ !
5 Aaah! There's a big, black s_____ in the bath!
6 I'm very e_____ about our holiday in Africa next month.
7 I've got a lovely picture on the w_____ above my bed. It's a v_____ of New York from the top of the Empire State Building.

4 Complete the text with prepositions of place from the box.

above   behind   between   ~~in~~   in front of
next to   on   under

This is my room. There's a bed <u>in</u> the room. It's on the right and there's a TV on the left. There's a table ¹_____ the bed. The table is ²_____ the bed and the TV. There's a chair ³_____ the table and ⁴_____ the TV there is a shelf. Where is my wallet? Here it is, ⁵_____ the shelf. Where are my keys? Oh, I can see them. They're ⁶_____ the photo on the table. Now I can't see my mobile phone. Oh yes, it's ⁷_____ the table!

WRITING | Avoiding repetition

1 Choose the correct answers.

I live near the sea *and / because /* (*but*) I never go swimming.

1 My best friends are Karol and Luke. *They're / He's / We're* great.
2 My bedroom is dark *so / but / because* the window is very small.
3 There's a picture on my wall. *They're / It's / There's* a view of Venice.
4 Mario's is our favourite café. We often go *their / there / they're*.
5 I've got lots of DVDs but I don't have time to watch *they / it / them*.
6 I love computer games *so / but / because* I often buy them.
7 There are some shelves in the room *but / because / and* there are some books on them.

2 Replace the underlined phrases with one word.

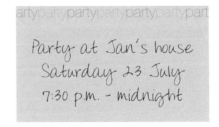

Party at Jan's house
Saturday 23 July
7:30 p.m. – midnight

Jake   There's a party on Saturday. <u>The party's</u> at Jan's house. <u>It</u>
Anne   Jan's house is easy to find. ¹ <u>Jan's house</u> is next to the school. _____
Jake   What about Lana, Lee and Carly? Can we invite ² <u>Lana, Lee and Carly</u>? _____
Anne   Lee and Carly can't come. ³ <u>Lee and Carly</u> have to work on Saturday. _____
Jake   The party starts at seven thirty. See you ⁴ <u>at the party</u>! _____

3 Complete the text with the words from the box.

but   he   it   so   their   them   ~~there~~
us   we

This is a photo of me in Budapest. We go <u>there</u> every year. My dad loves Hungary. ¹_____ likes the food. My mum likes ²_____ too. The two girls in the photo are my cousins. ³_____ always go to Hungary with ⁴_____ and ⁵_____ parents, my aunt and uncle. My aunt speaks Hungarian ⁶_____ she helps ⁷_____ in restaurants and shops. I want to learn Hungarian too ⁸_____ it's very difficult.

41

GRAMMAR

Countable and uncountable nouns

Nouns can be countable (C) or uncountable (U).

Singular and plural forms

Countable nouns have singular and plural forms.
Uncountable nouns do not have plural forms.

	singular	plural
	sausage	sausages
C	tomato	tomatoes
	egg	eggs
U	water	✗
	bread	✗

Numbers

We can use numbers with countable nouns:
one sausage, **two** tomatoes, **three** eggs

We can't use numbers with uncountable nouns:
one water, two breads

Mind the trap!

The word *money* is uncountable. However,
dollars, euros, pounds, etc. are countable:

one dollar, two euros, three pounds

Articles

We use indefinite articles (*a/an*) with countable nouns:
a sausage, **a** tomato, **an** egg

We can't use indefinite articles with uncountable nouns:
a water, a bread

We can use the definite article (*the*) with both countable and uncountable nouns:
the sausage, **the** tomato, **the** egg, **the** water, **the** bread

some and *any*

We use *some* and *any* with plural countable nouns and uncountable nouns.

We generally use *some* in affirmative sentences and *any* in questions and negative sentences.

Affirmative	I've got **some**	eggs.
Negative	I haven't got **any**	water.
Questions	Have you got **any**	eggs? water?

Measurements and containers

Measurements (litres, kilos, etc.) and containers (bottles, cartons, etc.) are all countable.
*Have you got **any** water?* (*water* = uncountable)
*Have you got **a bottle** of water?* (*a bottle of water* = countable)
*I've got **three bottles** of water.*

---

1 Write C for countable and U for uncountable. Write the plurals where possible.

sausage Ⓒ
sausages

water Ⓤ
—

1 tomato ☐
____

2 egg ☐
____

3 bread ☐
____

4 banana ☐
____

5 potato ☐
____

6 apple ☐
____

7 butter ☐
____

8 sugar ☐
____

9 biscuit ☐
____

10 milk ☐
____

2 Are they countable or uncountable? Write *a/an* or *some* and the correct (singular or plural) form of the noun.

some salad

1 _____
2 _____
3 _____
4 _____
5 _____
6 _____

3 Choose the correct words.

It's really hot outside. Have you got *a / some / (any)* cold drinks in the fridge?

1 There aren't *a / some / any* tomatoes, but there's *a / some / any* fruit.
2 Can I have *a / some / any* cheese sandwich and *a / some / any* bottle of water, please?
3 We can't make *a / some / any* pizza because we haven't got *a / some / any* tomatoes.
4 There are *a / some / any* biscuits, but there isn't *a / some / any* chocolate.
5 I'd like *a / some / any* vegetables and *a / some / any* chips with my fish.
6 Are you hungry? I've got *a / some / any* bread and there's *a / some / any* bottle of juice in the fridge.
7 Oh, no! We haven't got *a / some / any* birthday cake for Jerry. Have you got *a / some / any* eggs?

4 Look at the picture and correct the sentences. Use *some* and *any*.

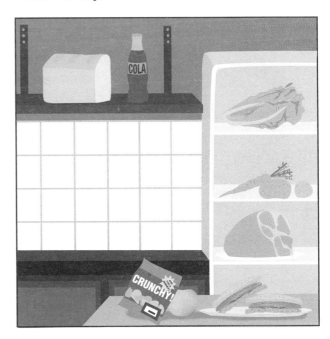

There's some cola in the fridge.
There isn't any cola in the fridge.
There's some cola on the shelf.

1 There are some sandwiches on the shelf.
_____
_____

2 There is one apple on the shelf.
_____
_____

3 There are some crisps in the fridge.
_____
_____

4 There is some meat on the table.
_____
_____

5 Complete the questions in the conversation.

A We really need to go shopping, the fridge is empty! I think we have to buy something to drink. Is there any cola? (there/cola)
B Yes, there are two bottles. [1] _____ (there/crisps)?
A No, there aren't any. [2] _____ (there/chocolate)?
B Yes, there are a few bars. [3] _____ (there/bread)?
A Yes, there is some. [4] _____ (there/butter)?
B No, there isn't. We need to buy some butter. [5] _____ (there/sausages)?
A Yes, there are some. [6] _____ (there/fruit juice)?
B No, there isn't any. We need to buy some juice. [7] _____ (there/vegetables)?
A Only some potatoes and carrots. I think we need to buy some tomatoes.

43

READING

1 Match the types of food to the correct pictures.

1 French food ☐ 3 seafood ☐
2 fast food ☐ 4 vegetarian food ☐

2 **[T26]** Read and listen to the restaurant reviews. Match the restaurants with the types of food in Exercise 1 that they serve.

A The Beach House ☐
B Govinda ☐
C L'Auberge ☐
D Burger Heaven ☐

3 Read the text again. Match the sentences with the restaurants.

This restaurant is by the sea.	A
1 This restaurant is part of a hotel.	☐
2 This restaurant is next to a cinema.	☐
3 This restaurant specialises in seafood.	☐
4 The owner is American.	☐
5 This restaurant doesn't serve any meat.	☐
6 This restaurant is good for a quick meal.	☐
7 The owner also has a restaurant in London.	☐
8 This restaurant grows its own vegetables.	☐
9 This restaurant serves vegetarian and meat dishes.	☐
10 This restaurant is good for weddings.	☐

Food

Out & About: Restaurants

A The Beach House

Lansford Dyke, Lansford, CLM2 6TF.
☎ *0565 879 7979.*
beachhouse@fastmail.net

The name tells you exactly where to find **The Beach House**: it's by the sea. And the owner, Mark Roberts, knows exactly what he wants.

'My idea is very simple. I want **The Beach House** to have fantastic food and a great atmosphere. We specialise in fish and seafood and we're right next to the sea, so everything is fresh and excellent quality. I love seafood so this is my dream restaurant.'

The Beach House also serves vegetarian and meat dishes for those who are not seafood lovers.

B Govinda

Paradise Square, Lansford, CLM1 8YY.
☎ *0565 748 9834.*
govinda@bignet.com

Govinda is a new Indian restaurant in the centre of town. The owner is Rajit Chowdah.

'There are a lot of Indian restaurants in Britain,' says Rajit, 'but **Govinda** is different. It is a vegetarian restaurant and it has traditional vegetarian dishes from all over India. We've got curries, of course – but we've got a lot of other dishes too.'

C L'Auberge

Bourne End, CLM9 5KD.
☎ *0565 937 9490.*
lauberge@bourneend.co.uk

L'Auberge is in the country outside Lansford, in the beautiful village of Bourne End. The owner is Pierre Songe of The Play House Grill in London.

L'Auberge specialises in traditional French cuisine. It is in a beautiful twelve-room country house hotel and it has its own vegetable garden.

Pierre says, 'I want **L'Auberge** to be a place for special occasions. When people celebrate their anniversary or get married, everything has to be perfect. We even make our own bread.'

D Burger Heaven

7 Bute Street, Lansford, CLM1 6HT.
☎ *0565 748 5733.*
burgerheaven@bignet.com

Burger Heaven is in the town centre next to the ABC cinema. The owner is Frankie Delaroux, from New York. Frankie has a clear vision for the restaurant.

'We keep it simple. We have burgers, salad and fries. It's fast, it's good and the price is right. That's it.'

GRAMMAR

> ## How much? How many?
>
> *How much...?* and *How many...?* are questions about quantity.
>
> We use *How many...?* with plural, countable nouns:
> ***How many*** *students are there in this class?*
>
> We use *How much...?* with uncountable nouns:
> ***How much*** *water have we got?*
>
> ## not much/not many
>
> In negative sentences, we can use *not + much/many*.
>
> We use *not many* with countable nouns:
> *There* ***aren't many*** *students in this class.*
>
> We use *not much* with uncountable nouns:
> *We haven't got* ***much*** *water.*
>
> We also use *Not many* and *Not much* as short answers to the questions *How many...?* and *How much...?*
>
> ## a lot (of)
>
> We use *a lot of* with both countable and uncountable nouns in affirmative sentences to talk about large quantities:
> *I drink* ***a lot of*** *coffee: about ten cups a day.*
>
> We can also use *not a lot of* with both countable and uncountable nouns:
> *There are***n't a lot of*** *female engineers.*
>
> We use *a lot* without *of* when we don't say the noun:
> *There's* ***a lot***.*/There are* ***a lot***.*

1 Complete the questions with *How much* or *How many*.

How many CDs have you got?

1 _____ DVDs have you got?
2 _____ money do you spend on clothes?
3 _____ brothers have you got?
4 _____ coffee do you drink?

2 Make the sentences negative. Use *not much* or *not many*.

I've got a lot of CDs.
I haven't got many CDs.

1 I've got a lot of DVDs.
_____

2 I spend a lot of money on clothes.
_____

3 I've got a lot of brothers.
_____

4 I drink a lot of coffee.
_____

5 I spend a lot of time on the Internet.
_____

SPEAKING

1 Who says the following? Write S for the shop assistant or C for the customer.

Can I help you? ⑤
1 Can I have a sandwich, please? ☐
2 How much is that? ☐
3 Anything else? ☐
4 That's £3.50 altogether. ☐

2 〔T27〕 Put the conversation in the correct order. Then listen to check.

a Great. Well, I'd like a chicken salad sandwich, please. ☐
b Good morning. Can I help you? ①
c That's £4.75 altogether. ☐
d Oh. Have you got any chicken? ☐
e Thank you. That's 25p change, your sandwich and your water. ☐
f Just a minute... yes, we've got chicken. ☐
g Thank you. Bye. ☐
h Yes. A bottle of mineral water, please. How much is that? ☐
i Here you are. Here's £5. ☐
j I'm afraid there isn't any ham left. ☐
k Certainly. Anything else? ☐
l Yes, can I have a ham salad sandwich, please? ☐

3 〔T28〕 Complete the conversation with one word in each gap. Then listen and check.

A Can I help you?
B Have you got ¹_____ cheese sandwiches?
A Yes, there's one ²_____ .
B Great. Could I have it, ³_____ ?
A Of course. Anything ⁴_____ ?
B No, that's ⁵_____ , thank you. How ⁶_____ is that?
A That's £3.50, please.
B ⁷_____ you are.

WORD LIST

Food and drink
apple
bacon
banana
biscuit
bread
burger
butter
cake
carrot
cereal
cheese
cheeseburger
chips
chocolate
coffee
cola
cream
crisps
egg
fish
flour
fruit
fruit juice
ham
jam
ketchup
lemonade
lettuce
margarine
meat
milk
oil
orange juice
peanut butter
peanuts
pizza
potato
rice
salad
salad dressing
sandwich
sausage
smoothie
sugar
sweets
tomato
tuna
vegetable
water

Containers/Amounts
bag
bar
bottle
box
can (n)
carton
cup
glass
jar
kilo
packet
spoonful
tin
tub

Healthy/unhealthy eating
animal fat
balanced
calorie
energy
fast food

health
junk food
takeaway
vegetable fat
vitamin

Prices
altogether
cent
dollar
euro
penny/pence
pound

Other
absorb
actually
agree
allergic (to)
anxious
awake
bad
birthday cake
boil
bring
call
casual clothes
choice
comfortable
contact (v)
contact details
contain
cook book
customer
decide
delicious
disease
everyone
exercise (v, n)
expert (on)
feel
fried
fry
get angry
greengrocer's
half
help yourself
idea
invitation
join
keep
knowledge
lifestyle
litre
make
miss
once
phone-in show
pick (n)
possible
protect (against)
reason
river
school hall
shoe
skin
some
spot
square
starve
store
strict
treat
worry
Yuck!

VOCABULARY

1 Write the names of the food items. The first letter of each word is given.

lettuce

1 c_____   2 c_____
3 c_____   4 h_____
5 m_____   6 p___
7 s_____   8 t_____
9 f_____   10 v_____

2 Complete the second sentence with one word from the box so that it has the same meaning as the first sentence. There are two words that you don't need.

allergic   boil   disease   ~~fried~~   greengrocer's
knowledge   takeaway   treat

These eggs are cooked in oil.
These eggs are <u>fried</u>.

1 Cook the potatoes in water.
_____ the potatoes.
2 I always buy apples at the shop that sells fruit and vegetables.
I always buy apples at the _____ .
3 I know a lot about Italian food.
I've got a good _____ of Italian cooking.
4 I can't cook so I often buy Chinese food which I take home with me.
I can't cook so I often buy a Chinese _____
5 I can't eat cheese because I get strange spots.
I can't eat cheese because I'm _____ to it.

46

3 Choose the correct answers.

I often have a bar / bottle / carton of chocolate in the morning.

1 How much is a *jar / bar / packet* of biscuits?
2 Could I have a *bottle / jar / packet* of jam, please?
3 There's a *carton / bar / packet* of milk in the fridge.
4 Can I buy a *packet / carton / bar* of sweets, mummy?
5 This shop doesn't sell *packets / cartons / tins* of tuna.
6 I want to buy a *carton / box / bar* of chocolates for my mum.
7 We need a *jar / kilo / tin* of cheese.
8 Is there a *box / bottle / packet* of water in the fridge?

4 Write the prices in full.

£5
five pounds

90p
1 _____

€15
2 _____

50c
3 _____

$10
4 _____

5 Complete the compound nouns with words from the box.

animal   birthday   casual   cook   fast   fruit
junk   peanut   salad   vegetable

salad dressing.
1 _____ clothes
2 _____ cake
3 _____ or _____ fat
4 _____ butter
5 _____ or _____ food
6 _____ book
7 _____ juice

WRITING | Invitations

1 Match the headings in the box with the correct parts of the invitation.

address   contact details   date   occasion
things to take   time

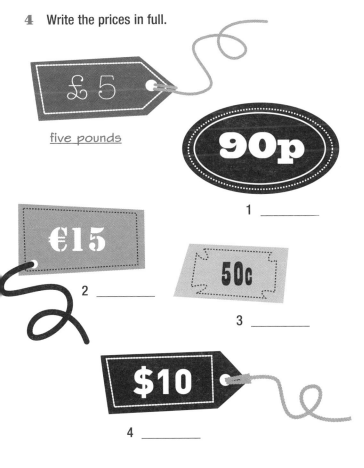

A birthday party!

Come to my birthday party → occasion
on Friday 15 December → 1
at 6 p.m. →
The party is at the Four Lions → 2
pub, near the public library.
The address is 27 Brompton → 3
High Street. Bring some food → 4
and your favourite music.
Call me on 0495768497 → 5
if you can come.

Jack

2 Complete the invitation with the phrases from the box.

7.30   address is 9 Seymour Close
some CDs and your dancing shoes
birthday party   04889 739799
Saturday 23 July

A birthday party!

Come to my ¹_____
on ²_____
at ³_____ p.m.
It's at my house.
The ⁴_____ ,
next to the school.
Bring ⁵_____ .
Email me or call me on
⁶_____ if
you can come.

Kara K

VOCABULARY AND GRAMMAR

1 Complete the sentences with one word in each gap. The first letter of each word is given. (8 points)

Where's the milk? It's in the <u>fridge.</u>

1 There are three s_____ with books on them in my room.

2 We've got an a_____ to sit on in the living room but there isn't a sofa.

3 There are dirty cups in the s_____ . Please wash them.

4 My desk at work has got a small d_____ in it. I keep my wallet there.

5 Please buy two b_____ of water and a p_____ of crisps.

6 I'd like a ham s_____ and a glass of fruit j_____ , please.

2 Choose the correct prepositions. (3 points)

What's that *in* /*on* the floor?

1 There is some food *in* / *at* the microwave. It's hot now.

2 There is a window *above* / *under* the cooker.

3 There is a chair *between* / *next to* the bed.

4 There is a spider *under* / *between* the sofa.

5 Our teacher always stands *in front of* / *behind* the board. He never sits down.

6 There's a clock *behind* / *between* the window and the door.

3 Choose the correct answer: a, b or c. (6 points)

I hate living in a house with three other students. <u>b</u> just one bathroom but that's not the only problem. I buy ¹___ food every Monday but there isn't ²___ in the fridge at the weekend. They eat it all. I've got ³___ bread in my room but I can't keep milk there. There ⁴___ food on the floor in my room because there ⁵___ cupboards. I haven't got ⁶___ money and I can't buy food for four people every week. But they just don't understand it. I think I need to find a new place.

	a There are	**b** There is	**c** Is there
1	**a** lots	**b** much	**c** a lot of
2	**a** any	**b** many	**c** some
3	**a** any	**b** many	**c** some
4	**a** aren't many	**b** is a lot of	**c** are a lot of
5	**a** aren't any	**b** isn't many	**c** is a lot of
6	**a** much	**b** many	**c** lots

4 Write questions using the words below and the correct forms of *there is*, *there are*, *how much* and *how many*. Then complete the answers. (8 points)

a sofa / in your living room?

A <u>Is there a sofa in your living room?</u>

B Yes, <u>there is.</u>

1 money / you spend on pizza?

A _____

B I spend a _____ . I eat pizza for lunch every day.

2 biscuits / you eat / every week?

A _____

B Not _____ .

3 a washing machine / in your kitchen?

A _____

B No, _____ .

4 plants / in your bathroom?

A _____

B Yes, _____ .

5 Find mistakes with articles and rewrite the sentences correctly. (5 points)

Do you like the dogs?

<u>Do you like dogs?</u>

1 Do you live in big house?

_____

2 A pizzas in this restaurant are lovely!

_____

3 My sister has got the new purse.

_____

4 The computers are really useful for homework.

_____

5 Where's my book? It's in a living room.

_____

LISTENING SKILLS

6 **T29** Listen to a conversation about holiday houses. Answer the questions with one or two words. (7 points)

1 What is on the corner of Hill Road?
_____

2 Do all the cottages in Sea View Gardens belong to Sea View Cottages?
_____

3 Can you see the sea from the bedroom?
_____

4 What can you see from the kitchen?
_____

5 How many bedrooms are there in the cottages?
_____

6 How much is the cottage in July and August?
_____

7 How much is the cottage from September to June?
_____

COMMUNICATION

7 Complete the text with the words from the box. (6 points)

past across ~~get~~ turning turn corner straight

Right, children. Today is the school picnic and we have to walk to the park. Do you know how to **get** to the park? We start at the school. We go out of the school and ¹_____ left into Market Street. We walk ²_____ on for half a kilometre. We go ³_____ the cinema and then take the first ⁴_____ on the right. There's a bank on the ⁵_____ . The park is opposite the bank. We have to go ⁶_____ the road there at the traffic lights. Don't run! Is that clear?

READING SKILLS

8 Read the advert for a town in England. Match the headings a–i to the paragraphs 1–7. There are two extra headings. (7 points)

a Where to eat   f Shopping
b Coming by car   g Town history
c Where to stay   h Having fun in Bognor
d Making friends   i A nice place to go
e Coming by train

Total _____ /50

Bognor

COME TO SUNNY BOGNOR! WE'VE GOT EVERYTHING YOU WANT FOR A GREAT HOLIDAY!

1 ☐ The station is in the centre of town, only 1 km away from the beach and close to all the shops. You can travel to London every hour and also to Brighton and Portsmouth.

2 ☐ You can drive here easily from London. Take the A29 road and then follow the signs. There are lots of places to park in the centre of town and near the beach.

3 ☐ Bognor is by the sea and the beaches are beautiful. The water is clean and warm. There are also lots of things for children to do when the weather is bad. You can play sports, swim at the swimming pool or visit the circus.

4 ☐ The old town centre is busy and has something for everyone. There is a large supermarket with a free car park right in the centre of town. You can also buy books, clothes, CDs and toys.

5 ☐ Near the town centre is the beautiful Hotham Park. It is full of trees and gardens. You can have a picnic by the old house. It's a very quiet and relaxing place.

6 ☐ There are lots of great restaurants in Bognor. Traditional fish and chips next to the beach and Chinese, French and Italian food in the centre of town. There are also some lovely cafés for cakes.

7 ☐ You don't need to worry about accommodation in Bognor. There are a lot of hotels in the town. Many of the hotels have a view of the sea from the bedrooms. There are also guest houses and 'bed and breakfast' hotels in family houses.

49

I remember ...

GRAMMAR

Past Simple: *to be*

	Affirmative	Negative	
I/He/She/It	**was**	**was not (wasn't)**	at school yesterday.
You/We/They	**were**	**were not (weren't)**	

Yes/No questions		Short answers	
Was	I he she it	at school yesterday?	Yes, I/he/she/it **was**. No, I/he/she/it **wasn't**.
Were	you we they		Yes, you/we/they **were**. No, you/we/they **weren't**.

Wh- questions
Where were you last week?
Who were you with?
Why were you in London?

Past Simple: *can* for ability

	Affirmative	Negative
I/you/he/she/it/ we/they	**could** swim.	**couldn't** swim.

Questions	Short answers
Could I/you/he/she/it/we/ they swim?	Yes, I/you/he/she/it/we/ they **could**. No, I/you/he/she/it/we/ they **couldn't**.

1 Complete the sentences with the correct form of *was* or *were*: affirmative (+) or negative (–).

My brother <u>was</u> at home this morning. (+)
My parents <u>weren't</u> on holiday last week. (–)

1 Janet and I _____ at the cinema last night. (+)
2 You _____ at home yesterday. (–)
3 Both my sisters _____ at school yesterday. (+)
4 My friend _____ in Scotland last week. (+)
5 It _____ very hot last summer. (–)
6 We _____ late yesterday. (–)

2 Complete the questions and short answers.

<u>Were you</u> (you) at home last night?
Yes, <u>I was</u>.

1 _____ (your brother) at school yesterday?
Yes, _____ .
2 _____ (your parents) late for work on Monday?
No, _____ .
3 _____ (you and your friends) at the cinema on Tuesday?
Yes, _____ .
4 _____ (your mum) at a birthday party on Sunday?
No, _____ .

3 Complete the questions for these answers. Use appropriate question words.

'<u>Where were you</u> last night?' 'I was at the cinema.'

1 '_____ with?' 'I was with Nick.'
2 '_____ on Friday morning?' 'She was at school.'
3 '_____ the concert?' 'The concert was two days ago.'
4 '_____ late?' 'Because their train was late.'

4 Complete the questions and answers in the dialogue. Use the correct form of *can* and *could* and the words in brackets.

Marc — Can I ask you a few questions?
Monika — Of course.
Marc — <u>Could you speak</u> (you/speak) French when you were six?
Monika — No, I <u>couldn't</u>.
Marc — ¹_____ (you/speak) French now?
Monika — Yes, I ²_____ .
Marc — ³_____ (you/play) a musical instrument when you were at primary school?
Monika — Yes, I ⁴_____ . I ⁵_____ play the piano when I was five.
Marc — How many instruments ⁶_____ (you/play) now?
Monika — I ⁷_____ play three. My dad's a musician. He ⁸_____ play five instruments.
Marc — Wow! What about your mum?
Monika — She ⁹_____ play any instruments but she ¹⁰_____ sing.

GRAMMAR

Past Simple: affirmative

We use the Past Simple to talk about things which started and finished in the past:
- actions: *We **arrived** yesterday.*
- situations: *I **lived** in Singapore when I was a child.*
- routines: *Last summer I **studied** English for two hours every day.*

I/You/He/She/It/We/They	**watched**	football on TV	yesterday.

Regular verbs
Past Simple regular verbs end in **-ed**, e.g. work**ed**, play**ed**, start**ed**.

The spelling rules are:
- for most verbs, add **-ed**, e.g. finish**ed**
- for verbs ending in **-e**, add **d**, e.g. liv**ed**, lov**ed**.
- for verbs ending in a consonant + *y*, change *y* to *i* and add **-ed**, e.g. stud**ied**, tr**ied**.
- for verbs ending in consonant + vowel + consonant, double the final consonant and add *-ed*, e.g. stop**ped**, prefer**red**.

Irregular verbs
See Student's Book page 142 for a list of irregular verbs.

Mind the trap!

Some regular verbs that end in a vowel + consonant don't double the consonant. If the word has two syllables, we only double the last consonant when the stress is on the second syllable:

prefer – preferred

open – opened.

1 Put the Past Simple forms of the verbs from the box in the correct column in the table.

~~ask~~   chat   fry   hate   live   love   play
prefer   stop   study   work   worry

Past Simple			
+ -ed: *started*	**+ -d:** *danced*	**y + -ied:** *cried*	**double consonant + -ed:** *referred*
asked	3 _____	6 _____	9 _____
1 _____	4 _____	7 _____	10 _____
2 _____	5 _____	8 _____	11 _____

2 Complete the crossword with irregular Past Simple verbs.

ACROSS
1 have
3 see
6 take
8 make
9 are
10 think
12 give
15 read
16 meet
17 get

DOWN
2 drink
4 buy
5 come
7 go
9 write
11 tell
13 eat
14 leave

3 Complete the text with the Past Simple forms of the verbs in brackets.

When I was seventeen I _loved_ (love) punk music. I ¹_____ (see) lots of bands in concert and I ²_____ (buy) lots of records. We ³_____ (live) in Birmingham and my dad ⁴_____ (work) in a bank. I ⁵_____ (think) my parents were boring. Now I live in Coventry. And I work in a bank.

4 Complete the text with the correct forms of the verbs in the box. There is one extra verb that you do not need.

become   find   get   ~~meet~~   move   send
talk   walk   write

When I was in year eight, Hannah Barker was my best friend. We _met_ outside her house at 8.30 every day and ¹_____ to school together. We ²_____ about pop music and television and people at school. In year nine, her family ³_____ to Scotland. We ⁴_____ to each other for a few months, but then we stopped. Last year, I ⁵_____ her on Facebook. I ⁶_____ her a message and we ⁷_____ friends again.

5 Complete the sentences with *ago*, *last* or *in*.

I went to the cinema three times _last_ week.
1 I played in a band two years _____ .
2 I went for a run in the park _____ Saturday.
3 I spoke to her _____ week.
4 We went to America _____ 2006.
5 We had pizza _____ night.
6 We met for a coffee one week _____ .
7 I worked in a factory _____ the 1990s.

51

READING

1 Read the text and put the paragraphs in the correct order.

1 C 2 ☐ 3 ☐ 4 ☐ 5 ☐

THE AMERICAN BEATLES

A Some people said 'No'. When they started, only Mike and Peter were musicians. Davey and Mickey couldn't play instruments. They were actors. But they soon learnt and, in 1967, they played concerts. They really could play now.

B These TV shows made them very popular. In 1967 they sold more records than The Beatles and The Rolling Stones together. But there were questions. Were The Monkees a real band? Could they play their instruments?

C The Beatles made their first record in 1962. In 1963 they were big stars in Britain but not in America. They went there in February 1964 and America fell in love! In April 1964, the top five records in America were all Beatles records.

D After two years of concerts, records and TV shows, the band were unhappy. They wanted to write their own songs and be a 'real' band. In 1968, Peter left the band and the others soon broke up. They were only together for two years but they were the first boy band.

E Bob Rafelson and Bert Schneider saw The Beatles and had an idea. They decided to make The American Beatles. They found three young Americans, Mike, Mickey and Peter, and one Englishman, Davey. Songwriters wrote songs for them. They made their first record in 1966 and had their own TV show. They played their songs on the show – the first pop videos!

2 [T30] Read and listen to the article. Check your answers to Exercise 1.

3 Read the text again. Are the statements true (T), false (F) or is there no information (NI)?

1 The Beatles were popular in Britain before they were popular in the USA. ☐
2 The Beatles released five records in 1964. ☐
3 Bob Rafelson and Bert Schneider wanted to work with The Beatles. ☐
4 The Monkees knew each other before they joined the band. ☐
5 Not all The Monkees were American. ☐
6 The Monkees were very popular in 1967. ☐
7 Mike and Peter both played the guitar. ☐
8 Mickey and Davey learnt to play their instruments. ☐
9 Peter was the first person to leave the band. ☐

4 Read the sentences below. Write M for The Monkees or B for The Beatles.

Two of them were actors. [M]
1 They started in 1962. ☐
2 They once had the five top records in America. ☐
3 They broke up in 1968. ☐
4 They were all from England. ☐
5 They started in 1966. ☐
6 They had their own TV show. ☐

The Monkees

The Beatles

52

LISTENING

1 **T31** Listen to the three conversations and match them to the headings.

  1 Life was different. ☐
  2 A disappointing evening. ☐
  3 A good day out. ☐

Conversation A

Tim and Rachel

Conversation B

Sophie and Peter

Conversation C

Julie and Nick

2 **T31** Listen again. Are the statements true (T) or false (F)?

Conversation A

  1 Rachel went to London yesterday. ☐
  2 She went on her own. ☐
  3 Mark is her brother. ☐
  4 She had fun. ☐

Conversation B

  5 Peter's family was rich when he was young. ☐
  6 There were six children. ☐
  7 His father was a gardener. ☐
  8 His mum was a nurse in a London hospital. ☐

Conversation C

  9 Nick went to see Vixen last Tuesday. ☐
  10 He went on his own. ☐
  11 He thought Vixen were really good. ☐
  12 Andy hated them. ☐

SPEAKING

1 **T32** Choose the most appropriate response. Then listen to check.

Jenny	What's the matter?
Adam	I failed my driving test.
Jenny	ⓐ Never mind.
	b That's brilliant!
	c Well done!

1
Peter	How was your day?
Miranda	Great! I passed my Maths test.
Peter	**a** I'm so sorry.
	b Good for you!
	c Oh dear.

2
Nikki	How was your day?
Paul	Terrible! My girlfriend finished with me.
Nikki	**a** Good for you!
	b How fantastic!
	c I'm so sorry.

3
Heather	What's up?
Lucas	You know that book you lent me? Well, I lost it.
Heather	**a** Don't worry.
	b I'm so sorry.
	c Well done!

4
Eve	You look happy.
Jamie	Yes, I am. Arsenal won again!
Eve	**a** Well done!
	b Don't worry.
	c That's fantastic!

2 **T33** Match each statement to the correct response from the box. Then listen to check.

A Forget about it.   **B** I'm so sorry.
C Well done!

☐ **1** My computer stopped working. I lost all my photos, songs and schoolwork.

☐ **2** I thought your birthday was next week. I haven't got you a present.

☐ **3** I got 88 percent in my Maths test.

D Good for you!   **E** How fantastic!
F Never mind.

☐ **4** My sister got a job on TV.

☐ **5** The concert wasn't very good.

☐ **6** I worked really hard for these exams. I think I passed.

WORD LIST

School/University subjects
Algebra
Art
Biology
Chemistry
Economics
French
Geography
History
Information Technology (IT)
Languages
Literature
Maths
Music
Physical Education (PE)
Physics
Spanish
Trigonometry

Other
abroad
act (v)
add
advice
after that
ago
apologise
area
argument
ask (for)
bowling alley
boy band
brilliant
CD player
certificate
clearly
colourful
dark (n)
degree
drums
excellent
exchange programme
fail an exam
finally
first (adj, adv)
floppy disk
foreign language
funny
glad
glamorous
Good for you!
grade
hamburger
hold
hope (v)

imagine
improve
information
instrument
Internet access
Internet connection
karate
last (adj)
last night
leave school
little (adv)
lose
mad
make friends (with)
make-up
mood
musical
Never mind!
new romantics
news
north (adj, n)
order
pass an exam
PC
peaceful
personal
phone call
photograph (n)
pocket money
poor
popular
racing car
ride a bike
save
sciences
secondary school
share (v)
slow
somewhere
space
suggest
take an exam
talented
text (v)
then
toast
travel (v)
use
vegetarian (n)
waiter
website
wet
World Wide Web

VOCABULARY

1 Write the school subjects.

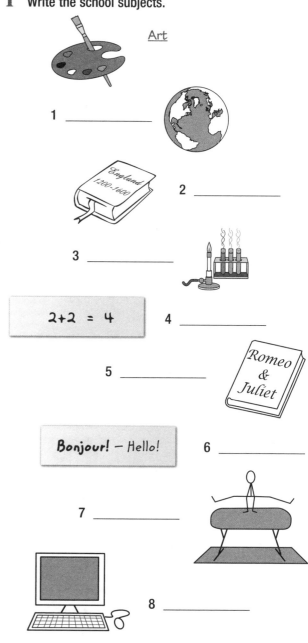

_____ Art

1 _____

2 _____

3 _____

4 _____

$$2+2 = 4$$

5 _____

6 _____

Bonjour! – Hello!

7 _____

8 _____

2 Complete the words.

You can l <u>e</u> <u>a</u> <u>v</u> <u>e</u> school when you are sixteen in England.

1 You get a d __ __ __ __ __ when you finish university.

2 All schoolchildren have to take e __ __ __ __ .

3 G __ __ __ __ __ tell you how good your work is. In some countries you get an A for good work. In other countries, you get a 5.

4 Chemistry, Biology and Physics are all s __ __ __ __ __ __ __ .

5 If you work hard, you will p__ __ __ your exams.

6 A c __ __ __ __ __ __ __ __ __ __ __ is a piece of paper you get when you finish a course or a year at school.

3 Complete the sentences with words from the box.

abroad   advice   colourful   floppy   foreign   ~~popular~~   secondary   somewhere   vegetarian

My cousin's band are really <u>popular</u> in their town.

1 Do you prefer holidays in your country or _____ ?
2 Can you speak any _____ languages?
3 We need to find _____ to practise before the concert.
4 I'm not a _____ because I eat fish.
5 I started _____ school when I was eleven.
6 Can you give me some _____ about summer work?
7 That's a very _____ painting. What is it?
8 Do you remember when computers had _____ disks?

4 Match the sentence halves.

I asked my teacher   [C]
1 My friend went on an exchange   [ ]
2 I really don't want to fail   [ ]
3 The library has got free Internet   [ ]
4 My grandfather left   [ ]
5 I find it difficult to make   [ ]
6 I don't get much pocket   [ ]
7 I could ride   [ ]

a school when he was fourteen.
b money from my parents.
c ~~for more time.~~
d friends.
e access for your laptop.
f programme to Spain.
g a bike when I was five.
h my Physics exam.

5 Choose the correct answers.

quiet: *popular* / (*peaceful*) / *colourful*

1 not in your own country: *abroad* / *area* / *travel*
2 very good: *popular* / *glad* / *brilliant*
3 a musical instrument: *karate* / *drum* / *new romantics*
4 next: *finally* / *first* / *after that*
5 get better at something: *imagine* / *fail* / *improve*
6 say sorry: *share* / *apologise* / *suggest*
7 something to eat: *order* / *make-up* / *toast*
8 very good at something: *talented* / *glamorous* / *mad*

WRITING | Email of apology

1 Read the email and put the paragraphs A–C in the correct order.

1 ☐   2 ☐   3 ☐

NEW MESSAGE   ☒

From: lols@abc.coo
To: Jamal
Subject: Hi!

A I hope you're not mad at me. See you at the Metallica concert? I've got their new CD – it's brilliant.
BIG kiss,
Lols

B Hi Jamal,
I'm sorry about yesterday. I told Jim I couldn't come to your party and I thought he told you.

C First of all, I had to have lunch with my dad and his girlfriend. He gave me £50, but it was really boring. They talked about their new house the whole time. Then I had to go home to finish my Maths project.

---

2 Match the paragraphs A–C with the headings below.

conclusion ☐   explanation ☐   introduction ☐

3 Complete the email of apology with words from the box.

all   hope   had   ~~how~~   really   see   that   then   was

---
NEW MESSAGE   ☒

From: diego@abc.coo
To: Sam
Subject: HowRU!

Hi Sam,
<u>How</u> are you? I ¹_____ you're not angry with me.
I had a ²_____ bad day and forgot to phone you.
First of ³_____ , I had a Maths exam in the morning.
It ⁴_____ terrible. After ⁵_____ I had to have lunch with my uncle. He's nice but he talks and talks!
⁶_____ I had to take my little brother to the beach. When I got home, I was tired and went to bed early.
Anyway, I hope you ⁷_____ a Happy Birthday! There's a party at Cara's house tomorrow. ⁸_____ you there.
Bye
Diego

---

08 What's new?

GRAMMAR

Past Simple: negatives and questions

	Affirmative	Negative
I/He/She/It/You/We/They	**watched** a film yesterday.	**did not (didn't) watch** a film yesterday.
	went to France last year.	**did not (didn't) go** to France last year.

Yes/No questions			Short answers
Did	I/he/she/it/you/we/they	**watch** a film yesterday?	Yes, I/he/she/it/you/we/they **did**.
		go to France last year?	No, I/he/she/it/you/we/they **didn't**.

Wh- questions

What did you do last week?
Where did you go?
Which cities did you go to?
Who did you go with?
Why did you go there?
How did you travel?
When did you get home?

> ### Mind the trap!
> We use the infinitive form of the verb (not the past form) in negative sentences and questions.
>
> She **didn't buy** the shoes. (NOT ~~She didn't bought the shoes.~~)
>
> Did she **buy** the shoes? (NOT ~~Did she bought the shoes?~~)

1 Some of the sentences and questions below are incorrect. Find the mistakes and correct them. Tick the sentences that are correct.

What did your dad invent?   ✓

I didn't ~~studied~~ French at school.   <u>study</u>

1 What you did on Saturday?   _____
2 Where you went on holiday?   _____
3 My uncle didn't make a lot of money.   _____
4 Did you like the film? Yes, I liked.   _____
5 Who you met in the park?   _____
6 Did Germany win the 2010 World Cup? No, they didn't.   _____
7 I didn't watch TV last week.   _____
8 Did you ate lunch? No, I didn't.   _____
9 My parents didn't had computers when they were young.   _____
10 I didn't buy anything yesterday.   _____
11 Did you worked yesterday?   _____
12 Which European countries did you visit last year?   _____

2 Complete the negative sentences.

Last week I got up at seven o'clock every day except Monday.

I <u>didn't get up at seven o'clock</u> on Monday.

1 Emma left the house at eight o'clock every day except Tuesday.
Emma _____ on Tuesday.
2 My dad worked every day except Wednesday.
My dad _____ on Wednesday.
3 My parents came home by train every day except Thursday.
My parents _____ on Thursday.
4 My sister and I had dinner with our parents every day except Friday.
My sister and I _____ on Friday.
5 I went to bed early every day except Saturday.
I _____ on Saturday.
6 The Internet connection worked every day except Sunday.
The Internet connection _____ on Sunday.

3 Complete the questions and short answers using the phrases in brackets and the correct form of the verb *do*.

Aina   <u>Did you go</u> (you/go) to France for your holidays?

Carlos   Yes, we <u>did</u>. We went to Paris.

Aina   [1]_____ (you/have) a good time?

Carlos   Yes, we [2]_____ . It was great!

Aina   [3]_____ (you/visit) the Louvre?

Carlos   No, we [4]_____ . My mother doesn't like galleries.

Aina   [5]_____ (you/go) up the Eiffel Tower?

Carlos   Yes, we [6]_____ . We went up the Eiffel Tower on the first day.

Aina   [7]_____ (your mother/like) it?

Carlos   Of course she [8]_____ ! Paris is her favourite city now!

Aina   [9]_____ (you/eat) in any good restaurants?

Carlos   Yes but only once. We ate fast food on the other days.

Aina   [10]_____ (your dad/take) any photos?

Carlos   No, he [11]_____ . He lost his camera but I took some photos with my mobile phone. Would you like to see them?

4 Complete the conversation. Use the words in brackets to make full questions and answers.

Tippex

Anne   What are you reading?

Jim   It's a book about Mike Nesmith.

Anne   I think I know who he was! (he/invent/ the Internet) <u>Did he invent the Internet?</u>

Jim   No, he didn't! That was Tim Berners-Lee.

Anne   So what [1]_____ (he/do)?

Jim   He [2]_____ (sing/in a band)

Anne   [3]_____ (he/sing/in The Beatles)?

Jim   No, he [4]_____ (not/sing in The Beatles)!

Anne   Oh. What band [5]_____ (he/sing/in)?

Jim   He [6]_____ (sing/in The Monkees) They were called the 'American Beatles'. His mother was famous, too.

Anne   [7]_____ (she/sing)?

Jim   No, [8]_____ (she/not).

Anne   What [9]_____ (she/do)?

Jim   She invented Tippex.

5 Write questions so that the words in bold are the answers. Use the question words from the box.

~~When~~   When   Who   What   How much Where   Where

<u>When did Apollo 11 land on the moon?</u>
Apollo 11 landed on the moon **in 1969**.

1 _____

Napoleon attacked Moscow **in 1812**.

2 _____

Marie Curie discovered **Radium**.

3 _____

Juliet loved **Romeo**.

4 _____

Real Madrid paid about **€94 million** for Cristiano Ronaldo.

5 _____

Leonardo da Vinci came from **Florence**.

6 _____

The Olympic Games started **in Athens**.

READING

1 [T34] Read the article about Facebook founder, Mark Zuckerberg, and match the headings to the paragraphs. Then listen and check.

1 Money ☐
2 The idea ☐
3 Childhood Ⓐ
4 The website grows ☐
5 Early programs ☐

The Facebook Story

A _____

Mark Zuckerberg lived in Dobbs Ferry when he was young, 20 km from the town he was born in, White Plains, in the state of New York. He was born in 1984 and went to Ardsley High School and he was a very good student. Later he went to Phillips Exeter Academy. He was different to most students. He enjoyed Latin and he liked reading Greek literature like Homer's *The Iliad*. Most students don't!

B _____

Mark's father worked in an office. Mark enjoyed making computer programs and he built one to help the workers at his father's office. He also developed a computer version of the game Risk and a music player called Synapse.

C _____

In the USA, lots of schools and colleges have a book with photos of all the students and teachers in it. Students keep it to remember their time at school. It is called a facebook. Mark looked at the Phillips Academy facebook and wanted to make a computer version but he didn't have time.

D _____

Zuckerberg left school to study at Harvard University and he still had the idea in his head. At university, he met Dustin Moskovitz and they became friends. They worked on Mark's idea together and made a computer facebook for Harvard. Later, they thought that other schools and colleges could use the program. It quickly spread to other colleges like Yale and Stanford. When they finished university, Zuckerberg and Moskovitz moved to California to continue work on their idea.

E _____

The original Harvard Facebook started in 2004. In 2006, they decided that anyone could join. It soon became very popular. In October 2007, Microsoft bought 1.6 percent of Facebook for $240 million. Zuckerberg is now one of the youngest billionaires in the world. He is worth about $4 billion!

2 Read the article again and answer the questions with a maximum of three words.

1 When was Mark Zuckerberg born?
_____

2 What subject, apart from Latin, did he like at school?
_____

3 Where did his father work?
_____

4 What do you call a college book with photos of all the students and teachers?
_____

5 Which university did he study at?
_____

6 Where did he and his friend move after university?
_____

7 Which company did Zuckerberg sell some of Facebook to?
_____

3 Put the events in the order they happened.

a Mark first had the idea for a computer facebook. ☐
b Mark moved to California. ☐
c Mark went to Phillips Exeter Academy. ☐
d Mark met Dustin Moskovitz. ☐
e Mark was born. ☐1☐
f Mark sold some of Facebook to Microsoft. ☐
g Mark went to Harvard University. ☐
h Mark went to Ardsley High School. ☐
i Mark made the first Facebook. ☐

58

GRAMMAR

Comparison of adjectives

Adjective	Comparative	Superlative
One syllable: **new**	new**er**	the new**est**
One syllable ending in vowel + consonant: **big**	big**ger**	the big**gest**
One syllable ending in -e: **nice**	nic**er**	the nic**est**
Two syllables ending in -y: **friendly**	friendl**ier**	the friendl**iest**
Two or more syllables: **interesting**	**more** interesting	**the most** interesting
Irregular: **good** **bad**	**better** **worse**	**the best** **the worst**

A Ferrari is **faster than** a Mercedes.
Physics is **more interesting than** Chemistry.
My cat is **the friendliest** cat in the world.

1 Complete the sentences with the correct forms of the words in brackets.

Gadget corner: digital cameras

	Motex	Sasco	Nosan
Weight	40 grams	80 grams	95 grams
Price	$295	$85	$30
Camera quality	★★★	★★★★	★
Easy to use?	★★	★★★★★	★★★

The Sasco is <u>heavier</u> (heavy) than the Motex.
The Nosan is <u>the cheapest</u> (cheap).

1 The Motex is _____ (expensive).
2 The Motex is _____ (good) quality than the Nosan.
3 The Nosan is _____ (bad) quality of the three camera phones.
4 The Motex is _____ (difficult) to use.
5 The Nosan is _____ (heavy) than the Sasco.
6 The Sasco is _____ (good) of all the phones.
7 The Sasco is _____ (easy) to use than the Motex.

SPEAKING

1 T35 Look at the information about the MP3 player and match the questions to the answers. Then listen to check.

4GB MP3 player
Make: Sasco
Dimensions: 8 x 3 x 1 cm
Weight: 28 g
Price: £8

	How high is it?	C
1	How wide is it?	☐
2	How much is it?	☐
3	How heavy is it?	☐
4	What make is it?	☐
5	How big is the memory?	☐

a Four gigabytes.
b It's a Sasco.
c ~~It's eight centimetres high.~~
d It's £8.
e It weighs 28 grams.
f It's three centimetres wide.

2 Read the conversations about new gadgets and complete the questions.

Conversation A

A I want to buy a new camera!
B What <u>make is it</u>?
A It's a Sonya.
B What [1]_____?
A It looks old-fashioned. It's black.
B How [2]_____?
A Quite big.
B How [3]_____?
A It weighs about 600 grams.
B How [4]_____?
A It's about £400.

Conversation B

A I've got a new computer screen!
B What [5]_____?
A It's a Technosonic.
B How [6]_____?
A It's 40 cm wide.
B How [7]_____?
A It's 30 cm high.
B How [8]_____?
A It's not very thick at all. About 3 cm I think.

3 T36 Now listen to both conversations and check your answers.

59

WORD LIST

Technology
about 3 centimetres long/ wide/high/thick
advanced
click on an icon
close/open a window/program
download/upload music
electric
graphics
Internet connection
invent
inventor
light
make (n)
measure (v)
memory
metal (adj)
per hour
petrol
plastic (adj)
press (v)
print out
processor
put in/take out the CD/disk
record (v)
save the document/changes
screen
sound (n)
technological
the 'on' button
turn off
turn on
weigh
weight (n)
wi-fi Internet
wind-up (adj)
word processor

Inventions
bicycle
blue jeans
car
digital camera
dishwasher
DVD
electricity
Game Boy
headphones
home computer
Internet
laptop
microwave oven
mobile phone
MP3 player
plane
remote control
telephone (n)
television
Tippex
trainers
video (cassette)
video (recorder)

Other
a couple of
a pair of
battery
born (adj)

card game
centimetre
cheap
classic (n)
clean
condition (n)
create (v)
disaster
end (v)
especially
essay
exciting
explain
fight (v)
find out
finger
genius
gram
heavy
honestly
in contact
include (v)
institute
keep in touch
kilometre
laugh
leave
look (n)
mainly
make (a lot of) money
millimetre
mistake
modern
move (v)
name (v)
newspaper
obviously
old-fashioned (adj)
on my own
online (adv)
ordinary
over
part
pink
pocket (adj)
probably
put on
relaxing
review (n)
reward
scientist
secretary
shape (n)
silver
strategy game
strong
stupid
successful
take off
the European Union
useful (adj)
violent
voicemail
waste of time
watch (n)
win
World Cup

VOCABULARY

1 Label the items in the pictures. The first letter of each word is given.

bi*cycle*

1   h_____

2   l____

3   v_____ c_____

4   s_____

5   M_____ p_____

6   h_____ c_____

2 Complete the sentences with one word in each gap.

I've got a new pair *of* jeans.

1 How many old school friends are you _____ contact with?
2 Don't forget to keep _____ touch when you go away.
3 Do you like being _____ your own?
4 Computer games are a waste _____ time.
5 This car can travel at 190 kilometres _____ hour.

3 Complete the words.

A person who invents things.   *inventor*

1 Find out how long, wide or high something is.
  m_____
2 Find out how heavy something is.
  w_____
3 You need this to make your car start.
  p_____
4 You need this to make your computer, television or dishwasher work.
  e_____
5 There are ten in a centimetre.
  m_____
6 You do this when something is funny.
  l_____

4 Match the words to make compound nouns.

on	c	**a**	camera
1 blue	☐	**b**	processor
2 digital	☐	**c**	~~button~~
3 Internet	☐	**d**	phone
4 microwave	☐	**e**	jeans
5 mobile	☐	**f**	Internet
6 remote	☐	**g**	oven
7 wi-fi	☐	**h**	control
8 word	☐	**i**	connection

5 Complete the description with the correct adjectives. The first letter of each word is given.

FOR SALE

A lovely family car. It's not very m<u>odern</u>, in fact it's very ¹o_____-f_____ but it works very well. It's quite small. It is 2.5 metres ²l_____ , 1.8 metres ³h_____ and 1.5 metres ⁴w_____ but it is perfect for a small family.

It's very ⁵c_____ because I wash it every day. I have to sell it quickly which is why it is so ⁶c_____ – only $50.
Contact me on 02234 5645453.

FOR SALE $50
1.8 metres
1.5 metres
2.5 metres

6 Complete the sentences using one word from each box.

click find print put take turn ~~turn~~

in off on ~~on~~ out out out

When you want to use the computer, you have to <u>turn</u> it <u>on</u>.
1 Decide what you want to do and _____ _____ the right icon.
2 You can _____ _____ a lot about computers by reading articles on the Internet.
3 Don't forget to _____ _____ the computer when you go to bed.
4 Write your homework on the computer, _____ it _____ and give it to your teacher.
5 _____ the CD _____ here and it will start playing automatically.
6 _____ the DVD _____ when it's finished and put it in its box.

WRITING | Lost! notice

1 Look at the notice and choose the correct words to complete sentences 1–6.

Lost camera!

- Silver Sonya MX100 digital camera in a purple bag
- Old-fashioned and heavy
- Left in the library last Tuesday afternoon
- If you've found it, please phone Jan on 0302 433578

REWARD! €10

The Lost! notice **should**:
have a big / *small* heading.
1 have a photo of *you* / *the lost item*.
2 use *bullet points* / *full paragraphs*.
3 have a *long* / *simple* description.
4 *ask for money* / *offer a reward*.
5 include *contact details* / *age and surname*.
6 give information about *who lost it, how and why* / *what was lost, where and when*.

2 Use the phrases a–j to complete the gaps 1–7 in the *Lost!* notice. There are three extra phrases that you don't need.

a Left in
b Avatar DVD
c It's a DVD of that film Avatar. I saw it in January and it was great so I wanted to buy the DVD.
d In plastic bag from Diamond DVD shop
e yesterday afternoon
f 0122 343 287 (mobile)
g I'm very upset! I bought it at Diamond DVD shop for €9.99 and then went to Mick's Café with my friend Sam.
h phone Tim on:
i at about 3.30 yesterday afternoon, just after we'd finished school
j A cola and a pizza!

LOST! DVD!
1 _____
2 _____
3 _____ Mick's Café 4_____
If you've got it, 5_____
6 _____
REWARD: 7_____

VOCABULARY AND GRAMMAR

1 Write the correct school subject next to each question. (5 points)

In which subject do you:
do drawing and painting? <u>Art</u>

1 learn about the past? _____
2 use numbers? _____
3 read books and plays? _____
4 play sports? _____
5 study Chemistry, Physics and Biology? _____

2 Choose the correct answer. (4 points)

What time do you have English *degrees* / *lessons*?

1 I want to *end* / *leave* university and become a musician.
2 David's parents were really angry when he *passed* / *failed* his Maths exam.
3 I want to get a university *degree* / *certificate* in Geography.
4 If you want to *save* / *send* changes, click 'Yes'.
5 I got a good *grade* / *course* for my homework.
6 We *got* / *took* an English test yesterday. It was very easy.
7 I send text *news* / *messages* to my friends every day.
8 Put your dirty jeans into the *washing* / *clothes* machine.

3 Complete the text with the correct forms of the verbs from the box. (8 points)

not like   learn   be   ~~be~~   can   not have   go
meet   play

When I <u>was</u> at school my favourite subjects
¹_____ IT and Languages. I loved IT but
I ²_____ Music. I ³_____ play any instruments
and I was bad at singing but I ⁴_____ football
very well. I ⁵_____ to a school in London.
We were very busy during the week and we
⁶_____ a lot but we ⁷_____ lessons on Saturday
or Sunday. We were free to do what we wanted
for two days! On Saturday evening, I ⁸_____ my
friends at the cinema or a café. Then on
Sundays, I had to do my homework and get
ready for school again!

4 Write questions in the Past Simple. (4 points)

Why / you / miss school / yesterday
<u>Why did you miss school yesterday?</u>

1 How old / you / be / when / you / get your first bike
_____

2 Where / you / spend / your last holiday
_____

3 Can / you / use a computer / when / you / be / ten
_____

4 What / your best friend / do / last night
_____

5 Complete the advertisement with the correct forms of the adjectives in brackets. (6 points)

MASON'S CLOTHES

WHERE SHOPPING IS <u>easier</u> (easy)
THAN **ABC**!

Buy your clothes here!
We have ¹_____ (good) clothes in town.
Our prices are ²_____ (cheap) than
any other shops and our shop assistants
are ³_____ (friendly)
than anywhere else.
Come and see ⁴_____ (new)
and ⁵_____ (hot) fashions in Britain.

Mason's Clothes – can you find
a ⁶_____ (good) shop than this?

6 Choose the correct words to complete the sentences. (3 points)

Computers are more useful <u>c</u> TVs.
a that   b from   ⓒ than
1 I want the ___ expensive computer you've got.
a more   b most   c best
2 At my school, French is ___ popular than German.
a most   b the most   c more
3 I bought ___ smallest phone I could find.
a the   b a   c –
4 This bike is ___ than mine.
a big   b bigger   c the biggest
5 I got ___ grades than my friends.
a worse   b the worst   c bad
6 Is this CD player ___ cheaper than the other one?
a the   b a   c –

LISTENING SKILLS

7 🔊 **T37** Listen to six people talking about childhood memories. Match the speakers 1–6 to the memories a–g. There is one extra memory. (6 points)

Who remembers
a a special present? ☐
b a change in the home? ☐
c a lesson? ☐
d something that often happened? ☐
e a new family? ☐
f friendly help? ☐
g a sad parent? ☐

READING SKILLS

8 Read the website. Are the statements true (T), false (F) or is there no information (NI)? (8 points)

1 The film festival will show all of the films the writer mentions. ☐
2 The writer likes *Casablanca* because of the technology it uses. ☐
3 Humphrey Bogart doesn't tell Ingrid Bergman about his plans for her and her husband. ☐
4 It wasn't easy to decide on the funniest film. ☐
5 The best part of *The Producers* is when the two main characters meet. ☐
6 *Independence Day* was filmed in the summer. ☐
7 There are sadder films than *Brassed Off*. ☐
8 *Brassed Off* is sad at the end. ☐

COMMUNICATION

9 Complete the conversations with the words and phrases from the box. (6 points)

What's the matter?   Well done!
You look happy!   Don't worry!
How was your day?   ~~What's up?~~
I'm so sorry.

A <u>What's up?</u> You look sad.
B Yes, my dog died.
A Oh dear. ¹_____

A ²_____
B I forgot to send a letter and my dad's angry.
A ³_____

A ⁴_____
B Great! I got a summer job.
A That's brilliant! ⁵_____

A ⁶_____
B Yes, I met a beautiful girl at the disco last night.
A How fantastic! Good for you!

Total [____] /50

Complete our survey below and you could **WIN** tickets to the 'yourbestfilms.com film festival' in June – three days of films and talks. Fill the boxes with your choices and reasons using between 50 and 100 words in EACH section.

① Best film
For me, the best film ever is *Casablanca*. I know it's old and technology is much better now but nobody is cooler than Humphrey Bogart. It's his best film – he is strong but romantic. When he helps Ingrid Bergman and her husband to escape, but you think (and she thinks) that he is going with her … Brilliant!

② Funniest film
I love comedies and it is very difficult to say which is the funniest. I think it is *The Producers*. It's a story about two men who are trying to find the worst play in the world. It's great and the main actor, Zero Mostel, is amazing. I think the funniest part is at the start when he meets Gene Wilder and they have this great idea to become rich. And all the rest is just … well, worth watching!

③ Most exciting film
I know it's crazy, but I love *Independence Day*. It's true that it's a typical summer movie and the story is sometimes absurd, like when they find the president's wife. You also know how it will finish from the very beginning, but the special effects and the main actors are fantastic. I love it when Will Smith hits the alien and says 'Welcome to Earth', and many other scenes. Some people say it's the most stupid film. In some ways it is, but I love it anyway.

④ Saddest film
I don't really watch sad films but one film that always makes me cry is *Brassed Off*. It's not the saddest film but it's the best sad film. It's about a group of musicians. They all lose their jobs. One man hasn't got any money and he loses his home and then his wife and children leave him. His father is dying and he tries to kill himself. But it has got a happy ending and sometimes it's very funny – funnier than most comedies.

GRAMMAR

Present Continuous

The Present Continuous shows that an action is in progress now.

	Affirmative	Negative
I	am ('m) working.	am not ('m not) working.
You/We/They	are ('re) working.	are not (aren't) working.
He/She/It	is ('s) working.	is not (isn't) working.

Yes/No questions			Short answers
Am	I		Yes, I am. No, I'm not.
Are	you we they	working?	Yes, we/you/they are. No, you/we/they aren't.
Is	he she it		Yes, he/she/it is. No, he/she/it isn't.

Wh- questions
What are you doing?
Why are you laughing?
Where are you going?
Who are you talking to?

Spelling rules:

- For most verbs, add **-ing**: go → go**ing**, walk → walk**ing**

- For verbs ending with a silent -e, drop the -e and add -ing: take → tak**ing**, come → com**ing**

- For verbs ending consonant + vowel + consonant, double the last consonant and add -ing: put → pu**tting**, get → ge**tting**

- We don't double the consonant of two-syllable words when the stress is on the first syllable: open → open**ing**, begin → begin**ning**

- When the final consonant is -y, do not double it: pay → pay**ing**, say → say**ing**

- For verbs ending in -ie, drop the -ie and add -y: die → d**ying**, lie → l**ying**

1 Write the -ing form of the verbs.

	do	_doing_	6	stay	_____
	write	_writing_	7	study	_____
1	enjoy	_____	8	swim	_____
2	have	_____	9	take	_____
3	play	_____	10	talk	_____
4	read	_____	11	watch	_____
5	sit	_____	12	work	_____

2 Complete the postcard. Use the Present Continuous form of the verbs in brackets.

CORFU – SEAGULL HOTEL

Dear Giselle,
I 'm writing (write) to you from Corfu. We're in a great hotel. Jack and I ¹_____ (sit) next to the pool. Jack is very relaxed. He ²_____ (not worry) about work. He ³_____ (read) the paper. It's good for the children, too. They ⁴_____ (not watch) television and they ⁵_____ (not play) computer games. They ⁶_____ (swim) in the pool. And, I'm very happy. I ⁷_____ (not teach) and I ⁸_____ (not clean) the house. I ⁹_____ (listen) to songs on my MP3 player and I ¹⁰_____ (get) brown in the sun! The weather is beautiful. We ¹¹_____ (have) a wonderful time.
See you soon,
Siobhan

3 Complete the conversation using the phrases in brackets.

A Clara?
B What, Mum?
A _What are you doing?_ (what/you/do?)
B ¹_____ (I/study) for my Maths exam.
A I can hear voices. ²_____ (you/watch television?)
B No, ³_____ (I/not)!
A Yes, you are! ⁴_____ (you/not study), ⁵_____ (you/watch television)!
B ⁶_____ (I/not/watch television), ⁷_____ (I/listen to the radio).
A ⁸_____ (Why/you/listen to the radio?)
B ⁹_____ (I/have/a break). ¹⁰_____ (you/make) dinner?
A Yes, ¹¹_____ (I/be). Come downstairs. You can listen to the radio in the kitchen and help me at the same time.
B: OK Mum, ¹²_____ (I/come)! I am really hungry so let's hurry up!

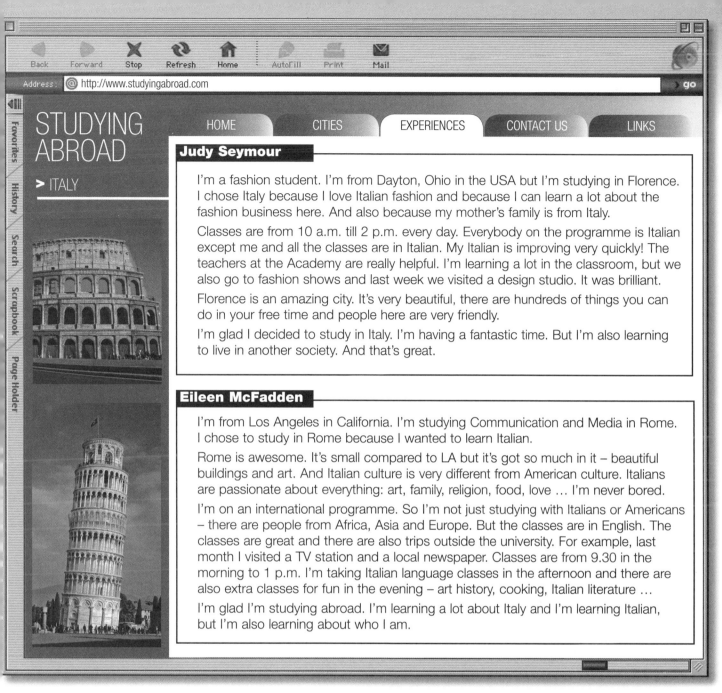

STUDYING
ABROAD

> ITALY

HOME   CITIES   EXPERIENCES   CONTACT US   LINKS

Judy Seymour

I'm a fashion student. I'm from Dayton, Ohio in the USA but I'm studying in Florence. I chose Italy because I love Italian fashion and because I can learn a lot about the fashion business here. And also because my mother's family is from Italy.

Classes are from 10 a.m. till 2 p.m. every day. Everybody on the programme is Italian except me and all the classes are in Italian. My Italian is improving very quickly! The teachers at the Academy are really helpful. I'm learning a lot in the classroom, but we also go to fashion shows and last week we visited a design studio. It was brilliant.

Florence is an amazing city. It's very beautiful, there are hundreds of things you can do in your free time and people here are very friendly.

I'm glad I decided to study in Italy. I'm having a fantastic time. But I'm also learning to live in another society. And that's great.

Eileen McFadden

I'm from Los Angeles in California. I'm studying Communication and Media in Rome. I chose to study in Rome because I wanted to learn Italian.

Rome is awesome. It's small compared to LA but it's got so much in it – beautiful buildings and art. And Italian culture is very different from American culture. Italians are passionate about everything: art, family, religion, food, love … I'm never bored.

I'm on an international programme. So I'm not just studying with Italians or Americans – there are people from Africa, Asia and Europe. But the classes are in English. The classes are great and there are also trips outside the university. For example, last month I visited a TV station and a local newspaper. Classes are from 9.30 in the morning to 1 p.m. I'm taking Italian language classes in the afternoon and there are also extra classes for fun in the evening – art history, cooking, Italian literature …

I'm glad I'm studying abroad. I'm learning a lot about Italy and I'm learning Italian, but I'm also learning about who I am.

READING

1 (T38) Read and listen to part of a website about studying abroad and complete the table.

	Judy	Eileen
Where is she from?	¹Dayton, Ohio _____	⁴ _____ _____
What is she studying?	² _____ _____	⁵ _____ _____
Where is she studying?	³ _____ _____	⁶ _____ _____

2 Read the text again. Are the statements true (T), false (F) or is there no information (NI)?

Eileen thinks Rome is boring.   ☑ F

1 Judy's mother speaks Italian.   ☐
2 Judy has classes for four hours every day.   ☐
3 Eileen's classes are all in the afternoon.   ☐
4 Eileen goes to three extra classes in the evenings.   ☐
5 There isn't much to do in Florence.   ☐
6 Eileen appeared on TV.   ☐

3 Read the website again. Write J for Judy or E for Eileen.

She thinks Italians are passionate.   ☑ E

1 Her classes are in English.   ☐
2 She visited a design studio.   ☐
3 Her mother's family are from Italy.   ☐
4 She's studying in Italian.   ☐
5 She's studying with people from all over the world.   ☐
6 She can take extra classes in the evening.   ☐

GRAMMAR

Present Simple and Present Continuous

We use the Present Simple to talk about routines and permanent situations:

*I **do** my Maths homework every Tuesday.*

HOMEWORK				
Monday	Tuesday	Wednesday	Thursday	Friday
English	Maths	History	Physics	FREE

We use the Present Continuous to talk about:
* an action that is in progress at the moment of speaking:
  *I can't come out – I**'m doing** my Maths homework.*

* an action that is in progress 'around' now, e.g. *My brother **is studying** at university.* (= He is somewhere in the middle of the course – the course is not finished.)

* a situation that is temporary, e.g. *I**'m studying** in Rome at the moment.*

Time adverbs help to show the meaning:
*I **eat** in a restaurant **every day**.*
*I**'m eating** at home **today**.*

Some verbs are generally not used in the Present Continuous (e.g. *like, love, hate, want, need, know, believe*), because they do not usually describe actions.

1 Which time adverbs do you use with the Present Simple and which with the Present Continuous? Write S for the Present Simple and C for the Present Continuous.

every day	S	
today	C	
1 usually	☐	**4** normally ☐
2 sometimes	☐	**5** this week ☐
3 at the moment	☐	**6** right now ☐
		7 all the time ☐
		8 never ☐

2 Choose the correct answers.

Usually, I cycle / *I'm cycling* to school, but there's a problem with my bike so this week *I take /* I'm taking *the train.*

1 *We stay / We're staying* in the Wolvercote Arms Hotel this week, but normally *we stay / we're staying* in the Randolph when we're in Oxford.

2 *I read / I'm reading* all the time. At the moment *I read / I'm reading* a book about China.

3 Normally *I don't study / I'm not studying* at the weekend, but my exams are next month so *I study / I'm studying* a lot right now.

4 Today *I have / I'm having* a big lunch, but normally *I have / I'm having* a sandwich.

5 My brother *works / is working* in a bank. This month he's on holiday and *he travels / he's travelling* around the USA.

3 Complete the conversations with the Present Continuous and the Present Simple forms of the verbs in brackets.

Conversation A

A Hello?

B Hi Susie. Is Benny there?

A Yes, but <u>he's having</u> (he/have) a shower.

B What about Jasmine?

A ¹_____ (she/watch) the TV.
²_____ (you/want) to talk to her?

B Yes, please.

Conversation B

A Fiona, this is Adam. He's from Poland.
³_____ (he/stay) with us this month.

B Hello, Adam.

C Hello. Pleased to meet you.

B So, what ⁴_____ (you/do) in Britain?

C ⁵_____ (I/study) English.

B Really? Where ⁶_____ (you/study)?

C At ELIC.

B Oh. ⁷_____ (I/know) somebody at ELIC. ⁸_____ (you/know) Kate Goodman?

C She's my teacher.

B Amazing. Tell her we met. And where ⁹_____ (you/live) in Poland?

C In Warsaw. ¹⁰_____ (I/work) in an American company.

B ¹¹_____ (you/learn) English for your job?

C Yes. ¹²_____ (everybody/speak) English in the company.

SPEAKING

1 〔T39〕 **Make questions and sentences using phrases from the boxes and complete the two conversations. Then listen to check.**

A

Can you give me   Could you tell
~~Hi Andrew, what~~   I can give you
Sorry, did you   What do you mean
Shall I phone

B

by 'off peak'
~~can I do for you~~
the website address, if you like
me the time of the meeting
say dot com or dot co dot uk
some information about trains to London
you at six o'clock to wake you up

Conversation 1

A Hello. Lynn White speaking.
B Hi Lynn. It's Andrew.
A <u>Hi Andrew, what</u> <u>can I do for you</u>?
B ¹_____ _____ ?
A Eight o'clock.
B Eight! That's early. I hope I don't oversleep.
A ²_____ _____ ?
B Yes, please. That would be great.

Conversation 2

A Network South West. How can I help you?
B Hello. ³_____ _____ ?
A There's one at six and one at ten thirty. The one at ten thirty is an off peak service.
B ⁴_____ _____ ?
A It is cheaper than the early train. The ticket is £23. At six o'clock the price is £45.
B Can I buy a ticket on the phone?
A No but you can get one on the Internet.
⁵_____ _____ .
B Oh, yes, please.
A It's www.swtrains.co.uk
B ⁶_____ _____ ?
A dot co dot uk
B Thank you very much.

2 〔T40〕 **Complete the conversation. The first letter of each word is given. Then listen to check.**

A Summerfields International Languages. How c<u>an</u> I h<u>elp</u> you?
B Could ¹ y_____ g_____ me some i_____ about English courses?
A Certainly, sir. We have elementary, pre-intermediate and upper-intermediate courses.
B What ²d_____ you m_____ b_____ elementary?
A Elementary means that you have a small knowledge of English but have problems communicating and understanding.
B Hmm, I'm not sure what my level is.
A Shall I ³s_____ y_____ a brochure?
B A brochure? Yes, thank you. And is there any information on the Internet?
A Yes. I can ⁴ g_____ you the a_____ of our w_____ .
B Just a minute, let me get a pen. OK.
A It's www.summerfields.languages.co.uk
B Sorry, ⁵ d_____ y_____ s_____ language or languages?
A Languages.
B Thank you very much.

WORD LIST

Clothes
boot
coat
dress
glove
hat
jacket
jeans
shirt
shoe
shorts
skirt
suit
sunglasses
sweater
tie
trainer
trousers
T-shirt

Shopping
bakery
changing room
checkout
clothes shop
dairy products
do up
good deal
package/packaging
pick up
product
put down
put on
queue (n)
receipt
shop (v)
take back
take off
try on

Other
alternative
angel
answer the phone
appointment
at the moment
be right
beginner
bench
board
bore (v)
bored
bottom (adj)
bright
brochure
broken
cancel
carefully
catch a cold
cause trouble
check (v)
conference
correctly
cut
delayed
dentist
deposit
desk
diet (n)

director
disagree
elementary
emergency
enrol
excite
expense
eye-level
farm
fashion
fix
floor
fresh
Geometry
Greek
gym
hard (adj)
head (n)
hunger
lecturer
level (n)
lonely
look down
look out of the window
look up
match (n)
mean (v)
mess
mint (n)
neck
normally
offer (v)
on the way out (of)
operator
part-time (adj)
pick fruit
pleased
Portuguese
pupil
quick
receptionist
right now
safe
schoolwork
service (n)
sick
side
simple
sleepy
smart
smell (n)
smile (v)
sound (v)
speciality
stressed
stressful
take your time
technique
tennis racquet
this morning/afternoon/
   evening
throw away
timetable
tip
top (adj)
train (n)
trouble
walk around
website design

68

VOCABULARY

1 Label the pictures.

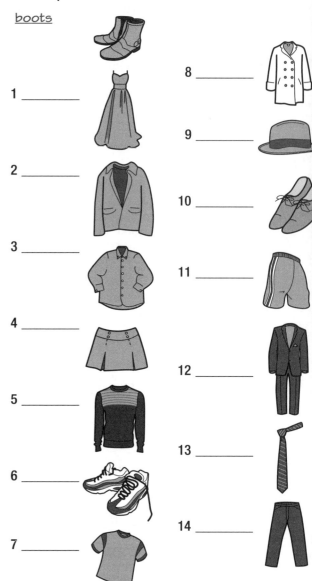

boots

1 _____
2 _____
3 _____
4 _____
5 _____
6 _____
7 _____
8 _____
9 _____
10 _____
11 _____
12 _____
13 _____
14 _____

2 Complete the sentences with the correct verb.

I have to go on a diet – I can't _do_ up my trousers.

1 That skirt is awful and it's very old – why don't you _____ it away?
2 It's raining – _____ your coat on.
3 It's hot – _____ your coat off.
4 I _____ my sunglasses down on the table for a moment and somebody stole them.
5 Look at this mess. _____ up your clothes and put them away in your wardrobe.
6 I hate this shirt and I can't _____ it back to the shop because I lost the receipt.
7 This dress is great and it's just your colour. Why don't you _____ it on?

3 Complete the words with one letter in each gap.

Try clothes on here.

c h a n g i n g   r o o m

1 Pay for things here in a shop.

c ___ ___ c ___ o ___ ___

2 Milk, cheese, yoghurt, etc.

d ___ ___ r ___   p ___ ___ d ___ ___ t ___

3 Buy bread here.

b ___ k ___ ___ ___

4 Stand in it and wait.

q ___ ___ u ___

5 Keep this, it tells you what you bought and how much it cost.

r ___ c ___ ___ p ___

6 Wear these on sunny days.

s ___ n ___ ___ ___ s ___ ___ s

7 They keep your hands warm on cold days.

g ___ ___ v ___ s

4 Complete the conversation with one word in each gap. The first letter of each word is given.

A Welcome to *English Quiz*. How many questions can our guest, Maria, answer? Here's question one. At school, teachers teach who?

B Students, no, p̲u̲p̲i̲l̲s̲!

A Very good! And who teaches at university?

B My uncle.

A Ha, ha. What's his job?

B He's a [1] l_____ .

A Very good. Now, nationalities. What nationality was Homer?

B Do you [2] m_____ Homer Simpson? He's American.

A No, the poet.

B He was [3] G_____ . He was from Greece.

A Very good. At the [4] m_____ , you've got three correct. Now, what nationality is Cristiano Ronaldo?

B Oh, he's from Portugal. He's [5] P_____ .

A Excellent. Now, jobs. Who looks at your teeth?

B A [6] d_____ .

A That's right. Last question. Who is the person in a hotel that gives you your room key?

B The [7] r_____ .

A Great. You answered all the questions [8] c_____ and scored six points!

5 Choose the correct answers.

You (were) / had / made right about Geometry. It's really difficult.

1 Could someone *answer* / *reply* / *talk* the phone for me, please?

2 Wear a sweater or you might *make* / *take* / *catch* a cold.

3 We've got plenty of time until the shop closes so *make* / *take* / *keep* your time.

4 I'm not trying to *cause* / *look* / *do* trouble, I just want to change these shoes.

WRITING | Messages

1 Read the note below. Twelve words are not necessary. Cross them out.

> Jack,
> I am sorry, I can't come to your party.
> My mum is ill. It is nothing serious but I want to stay home with her.
> There is a Jet concert next Tuesday. Do you want a ticket?
> Jane

2 Complete the note with the information from the conversation.

👤 Jack	Hi!
🌐 Chloe	Hello Jack. It's Chloe. Is Maria there?
👤 Jack	No, she's out. Can I take a message?
🌐 Chloe	Yes. I got the holiday brochures today. We can stay in a tent for €15 a night or we can get a room for €45. If we stay in the room, we have our own bathroom and we get breakfast. The campsite has hot water and looks nice. I have to book a place by Friday so can she ring me tomorrow?
👤 Jack	OK, I'll tell her.
🌐 Chloe	Thanks. Bye!

> Maria,
> Chloe rang. Holiday [1]_____ arrived [2]_____ .
> Two choices: Tent - €15 for a [3]_____ . Campsite has [4]_____ and looks nice. Room with own [5]_____ and [6]_____ for €45.
> Chloe has to [7]_____ by Friday - ring her [8]_____ .
> Jack

10 On the road

GRAMMAR

going to

We use *be* + *going to* + verb to talk about future plans or intentions, e.g. *I'm going to learn to drive this summer.*

	Affirmative	Negative
I	**am ('m) going to spend** August in the USA.	**am not ('m not) going to spend** August in the USA.
You/We/They	**are ('re) going to spend** August in the USA.	**are not (aren't) going to spend** August in the USA.
He/She/It	**is ('s) going to spend** August in the USA.	**is not (isn't) going to spend** August in the USA.

Yes/No questions			Short answers	
Am	I		Yes, I **am**.	No, I **'m not**.
Are	you/we/they	**going to spend** August in the USA?	Yes, you/we/they **are**.	No, we/you/they **aren't**.
Is	he/she/it		Yes, he/she/it **is**.	No, he/she/it **isn't**.

Wh- questions
What are you going to do this weekend?
When is your mum going to come home this afternoon?
How long are they going to wait?

> **Mind the trap!**
>
> When we use the verb *to go* with *going to* we write the verb twice:
>
> *I'm **going to go** to the cinema tonight.*

---

1 John and his friends are going to go on a tour of Europe. Complete what he says with the correct form of *going to* and the verbs in brackets.

Date	Country	City	See
Aug 1	Spain	Me – Barcelona	the Sagrada Familia Cathedral
		Anna and Tony – Granada	the Alhambra Palace
Aug 3	Italy	Me and Tony – Venice	St Mark's Square
		Anna – Pisa	the Leaning Tower
Aug 6	Greece	Me and Anna – Athens	the Acropolis

We **'re going to start** (start) our tour in Spain.
I ¹_____ (visit) Barcelona. Anna and Tony
²_____ (not come) with me. They ³_____
(go) to Granada to see the Alhambra. After
Spain we ⁴_____ (travel) by train to Venice.
Tony and I ⁵_____ (see) St Mark's Square in
Venice but Anna ⁶_____ (not join) us. She
⁷_____ (stay) with her friend in Pisa. I think
she ⁸_____ (climb) the Leaning Tower if it
is open. We ⁹_____ (sail) to Athens on the
ferry together. Anna and I ¹⁰_____ (take)
lots of photos of the Acropolis.

2 Put the words in the correct order to make questions about John's tour of Europe. Then look at the table in Exercise 1 and write full answers.

is / Barcelona? / do / going / in / to / What / John
<u>What is John going to do in Barcelona?</u>
<u>He's going to see the Sagrada Familia</u>
<u>Cathedral.</u>

1 Granada / are / in / going / What / to / Tony and Anna / see

_____

_____

2 to / go / going / Anna / Pisa / to / Is

_____

_____

3 go / is / in / Where / going / John / to / Greece

_____

_____

4 John and Anna / visit / to / Are / the Acropolis / going

_____

_____

READING

1 🔊 T41 Read and listen to the article. Match the people with the subjects they are studying and the jobs they want to do.

Subjects: Computing and Business
~~Modern Languages~~   Music and Performance
Politics and Economics   Anthropology

Jobs: ~~A job in tourism~~   Anthropology teacher
IT Service manager for a company
Piano player in a band
Work for the World Bank and the European Union

Josie: Modern Languages   A job in tourism
Howard: _____ _____
Xiuxiu: _____ _____
Tony: _____ _____
Marina: _____ _____

2 Read the article again. Are the statements true (T), false (F) or is there no information (NI)?

Josie is going to travel around Africa.   ☐ F

1 Josie is going to work for her uncle in Melbourne for three months.   ☐
2 Howard is going to work all summer.   ☐
3 Howard is going to start teaching in September.   ☐
4 Xiuxiu can only play one musical instrument.   ☐
5 Xiuxiu's going to live in Germany.   ☐
6 Tony's going to have a holiday before he starts work.   ☐
7 Tony's going to have a lot of responsibility.   ☐
8 Marina has never been to the USA before.   ☐
9 Marina has got a job in the European Union.   ☐

3 🔊 T41 Read and listen to the article again. Answer the questions with one or two words.

How long is Josie going to spend in Asia?
six months

1 How long is Tony going to spend in Turkey? _____
2 How long is Marina going to spend travelling around the USA? _____
3 Who is Tony going to go on holiday with? _____
4 In which city is Marina going to work in July? _____
5 How many countries is Josie going to visit before she gets to Australia? _____
6 When is Howard going to start his Master's degree? _____
7 What kind of music is going to be played at the festival in Germany? _____

What next?

This week *Student Magazine* talks to five students who are graduating this year. What are they going to do during their holidays?

Josie is studying Modern Languages at Sussex University.
First I'm going to take six months to travel around Asia. I want to see Vietnam and Thailand, Bali … Then I'm going to spend three months in Australia; I've got an uncle in Melbourne. Then I'm going to come home and look for a job and a place to live. I want to work in tourism.

Howard is studying Anthropology at Durham University
I'm not going to have a holiday. From July to September I'm going to work in a shoe factory. It's going to be hard but I really need the money to continue my studies. I'm going to start a Master's degree in Anthropology in September. One day I want to teach Anthropology in a university and do research.

Xiuxiu is studying Music and Performance at Guildhall University in London
First of all I'm going to go home for two months. My parents live in Nanjing in China and I really want to see them. Then I'm going to come back to London. I'm in a band with three other students from Guildhall. I play the piano. We're going to play at a jazz festival in Germany in October. Then we're going to look for more work.

Tony is studying Computing and Business at Kent University
I'm going to go to Turkey with some friends for two weeks in August. Then I'm going to start work. I'm going to work for my dad's company. The company makes sports clothes and equipment. About 400 people work there. I'm going to be the IT Services Manager. I love all sports – I play football and basketball and I run. So that's cool. But it's going to be a lot of responsibility.

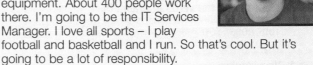

Marina is studying Politics and Economics at the LSE (London School of Economics)
I'm going to go to Washington in July. I'm going to work for the World Bank. That's going to be great, but it's just a temporary contract. I'm going to be there for six months. Then I'm going to take a month to travel around the USA. I'm going to come home to London in October and look for a permanent job. I want to work for the European Union, but it's hard to get a job.

GRAMMAR

must, mustn't, should, shouldn't, don't have to

must

- *must* is similar to *have to* (see Unit 4). We use it to talk about rules. It shows that it is necessary to do something: *Passengers **must show** their passport at passport control.*

- *must* is the same in all persons: *I/You/He/She/We/They **must arrive** at the airport two hours before the flight.*

mustn't and don't have to

- *mustn't* is the contraction of *must not*.

- *mustn't* is not the same as *don't have to*.

- *mustn't* shows that something is not permitted: *You **mustn't smoke** on the plane.* (= You can't smoke.)

- *don't have to* shows that something is not necessary but you can do it if you like – you have a choice: *You **don't have to wear** a tie at work.* (= You can wear a tie if you want to.)

should and shouldn't

- We use *should* and *shouldn't* for giving advice. *Should* is used to say that something is a good idea: *You **should buy** a good guide book.*

- We use *shouldn't* to say something is not a good idea: *You **shouldn't believe** everything people tell you.*

- *Should* is the same in all persons: *I/You/He/She/We/They **should take** regular exercise.*

Rules	You **must** do it.	It is **necessary**, you have to do it.
	You **mustn't** do it.	It is **not permitted**, you **can't** do it.
Choice	You **don't have to** do it.	You **can** do it if you want to, but it is **not necessary**.
Advice	You **should** do it.	It is **a good idea**.
	You **shouldn't** do it.	It is **not a good idea**.

---

1 Change the imperatives to sentences with *must* or *mustn't*.

Get a visa!
<u>You must get a visa.</u>

1 Don't forget to take your passport!
_____

2 Arrive at the airport before ten o'clock!
_____

3 Don't be late!
_____

4 Keep your bag with you at all times!
_____

5 Don't get on the wrong plane by mistake!
_____

2 What do they say? Complete the sentences with *must* or *mustn't* and the verbs in brackets.

Your boss: You <u>mustn't be</u> late and you <u>must work</u> hard. (be/work)

1 **Your doctor:** You _____ lots of fruit and you _____ . (eat/smoke)

2 **Your teacher:** You _____ your homework and you _____ in class. (do/talk)

3 **Your mum:** You _____ your room and you _____ out late. (tidy/stay)

4 **Your dentist:** You _____ me every six months and you _____ to brush your teeth at least twice a day. (see/forget)

3 Choose the correct answers.

You (mustn't) / *don't have to* smoke on the plane.

1 Passengers *mustn't* / *don't have to* wear their seat belts all the time.

2 You *mustn't* / *don't have to* run around in the swimming pool.

3 Students *mustn't* / *don't have to* cheat in exams.

4 Patients *mustn't* / *don't have to* use their mobile phones in hospital.

4 Write sentences with *mustn't* or *don't have to*.

Today's Saturday: *I / get up early*
<u>I don't have to get up early.</u>

1 Today's my mum's birthday: *I / forget to phone her*
_____

2 I want it to be a surprise: *you / tell anybody*
_____

3 There's plenty of time: *we / run*
_____

4 We're in the library: *we / talk*
_____

5 I passed all my exams: *I / retake any of them*
_____

6 You can finish this tomorrow: *you / do it now*
_____

5 Write advice. Use *should/shouldn't* and the ideas in the box.

> ask for help   get a Saturday job
> record the film and go out   go to bed earlier
> join a gym   make a sandwich   ~~text instead~~
> put on a jumper

> My mobile phone calls are very expensive.
> You should text instead.

1 I'm hungry.

_____

2 I'm cold.

_____

3 I never have any money.

_____

4 I can't stay awake in class.

_____

5 I don't understand these instructions.

_____

6 I want to be healthier.

_____

7 I want to go to a party tonight but there's a great film on TV.

_____

6 Ben and Melanie are going to Australia on a backpacking holiday. Complete the advice with *should* or *shouldn't* and the verbs in the box.

> be ~~go~~ keep stay swim travel

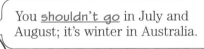

> You shouldn't go in July and August; it's winter in Australia.

> 1 Ben often loses things. He _____ his money and passport safe at all times.

> 2 Melanie, you _____ careful when you sunbathe. The sun is very strong.

> 3 You _____ in the sea if there are red flags on the beach; that means danger.

> 4 They _____ in youth hostels; they are good places to meet other backpackers.

> 5 Ben, we haven't got much money. We _____ by bus around Australia; it's cheaper than flying.

SPEAKING

1 **T42** Complete the conversation with the responses a–f. Then listen to check.

Karel I've got a week's holiday from work and I don't know where to go.

Eve <u>What sort of things do you like doing?</u>

Karel Well, I like going to art galleries and I like eating in restaurants.

Eve ¹_____

Karel I don't think so. I went to Italy in the summer.

Eve ²_____

Karel I'm not sure. It's a bit cold at this time of year.

Eve ³_____

Karel Yes, it could be fun. How much is it?

Eve ⁴_____

Karel Oh. It's very expensive!

Eve ⁵_____

Karel That's a good idea. I can paint the living room!

a Look there's the price – air fare and hotel included.

b Right. Well, if you don't want to go to Italy, what about Paris?

c Well, why don't you stay at home?

d If you like art, you could go to Venice. There's a special offer.

e Well, why don't you go to Barcelona? That's warmer.

f ~~What sort of things do you like doing?~~

2 **T43** Complete the conversations with words from the box. Then listen to check.

> about could don't good idea if
> ~~should~~ suggest (x2) sure think
> what (x2) why (x2)

1 **A** What <u>should</u> I buy my mum for her birthday?
   B What ¹_____ a pair of earrings?
   A That's a good ²_____ .

2 **A** I'm bored. What do you ³_____ ?
   B ⁴_____ you've got nothing to do, you could clean the house.
   A I don't ⁵_____ so.

3 **A** ⁶_____ can we do tonight?
   B ⁷_____ don't we go to the cinema?
   A Yes, ⁸_____ not?

4 **A** There's no food in the house. What do you ⁹_____ we do for dinner?
   B If you like Indian food, we ¹⁰_____ go to that new restaurant for dinner.
   A That's a ¹¹_____ idea!

5 **A** What about our holidays? ¹²_____ do you suggest?
   B Why ¹³_____ we go to New Zealand?
   A I'm not ¹⁴_____ about that. It's a long way.

WORD LIST

Accommodation
beach hut
campsite
guesthouse
hotel
youth hostel

Kinds of holiday
activity holiday
beach holiday
camping holiday
independent holiday
package holiday
touring holiday
working holiday

Transport
bus
car
coach
cycle (v)
ferry
flight
hitchhike
motorbike
plane
train (n)
underground

Souvenirs
baseball cap
calendar
doll in national dress
fridge magnet
key ring
mug
T-shirt
traditional food

Other
across
adventure
adventurous
allow
alone
animal conservation
Asia
balance (v)
beach
beauty spa
book (v)
border
bottled water
break (v)
building
camp (v)
change (v)
Channel Tunnel
charity
coast
coastal path
competition
cost (n)
dancer
dangerous
Denmark
destination
enter
entertainment
environment
excursion
experience
field
first-class (adj)
fly (v)
follow (an instruction)

get on with
give back
give sb a lift
go away
golf course
guide
hairdresser's
harm
hill
illegal
included in the price
instead
interview (v)
Ireland
irresponsible
journey
last (v)
member
Middle East
mountain
on the way
organiser
pack (v)
palace
passport
pen friend
place of interest
plan (n)
postcard
practical
prefer
race (n, v)
rail ticket
raise (v)
relationship
reporter
romantic
route
rucksack
sailing
sea
sensible
separate (adj)
serve
several
sight
sleeping bag
south (adj, adv)
sponsored
staff
stay (with sb/at a guesthouse)
stop
suggestion
suitcase
sunny
surfing
sweatshirt
swimming pool
Switzerland
take part (in)
take photos
take the train/ferry
tandem
tent
Thailand
through
touch (v)
tour (n)
traffic
travel agent
traveller
trip (n)
unpack
visa
volunteer (n)
waste (v)
water sports
water-ski

VOCABULARY

1 Label the pictures.

car

1 _____

2 _____

3 _____

4 _____

5 _____

6 _____

7 _____

2 Match the types of holidays to the descriptions.

beach holiday	C
1 package holiday	☐
2 activity holiday	☐
3 independent holiday	☐
4 camping holiday	☐
5 touring holiday	☐
6 working holiday	☐

A I booked all the transport and hotels myself. I didn't use a travel agent.

B My friends are going to spend the summer picking fruit in the south of France.

C I'm going to swim and lie in the sun.

D My parents are going to spend three weeks driving round Europe seeing as much as they can.

E It's going to be a busy two weeks. We're going to sail, climb, walk and do lots of other things.

F We're taking our tent to the mountains.

G It's great. We get the hotel, transport, bus from the airport to the hotel and all our meals for one price.

74

3 Make compound nouns from the words in the box and complete the sentences.

agent bag bottled coastal course fridge golf hostel magnet path ~~pool~~ sleeping sports ~~swimming~~ travel water water youth

The sea's cold but the hotel <u>swimming pool</u> is warm.

1 I only drink _____ _____ when I'm on holiday.
2 We can walk along the _____ _____ and look at the sea.
3 I want to learn some _____ _____ like surfing and sailing.
4 I need a nice warm _____ _____ for my camping holiday.
5 We can stay in a _____ _____ and meet some other young people.
6 There's a _____ _____ near the hotel so I may have a game while I'm here.
7 The _____ _____ in the centre of town has good holiday brochures.
8 Let's buy a _____ _____ for the kitchen.

4 Complete the missing words. The first letter of each word is given.

I <u>booked</u> my holiday on the Internet. My [1] f_____ to Madrid was at 6 o'clock in the morning so I [2] p_____ my bags the night before. There were no trains to the airport at that time so my mum [3] g_____ me a lift in her car. I didn't have a suitcase – I carried a [4] r_____ on my back. At Madrid, I bought a rail [5] t_____ for the train to Salamanca. At the hotel, I [6] u_____ my suitcase and fell asleep!

5 Complete the sentences with prepositions from the box.

~~away~~ in (x3) of on (x2) with

I'm going to go <u>away</u> for a few days.

1 I get _____ very well with my sister.
2 Are all meals included _____ the price?
3 We're not going to stay _____ a hotel.
4 We're going to stay _____ my aunt.
5 Let's stop for a picnic _____ the way to the hotel.
6 Are there any places _____ interest near the campsite?
7 I don't want to take part _____ the evening activities at the hotel.

LOUVRE
www.louvre.fr
VALABLE AU MUSEE CE JOUR
DATE: 11/MAI
MUSEE JOURNEE
11/MAI

WRITING | Postcard

1 Put the parts of the postcard in the correct order.

BARCELONA – SAGRADA FAMILIA

☐ A Tomorrow we're going to go to Sitges – it's a beautiful beach.
☐ B We're in Barcelona. We're having a fantastic time. Barcelona is beautiful and the weather is warm.
☐ C Dear Jenny,
☐ D See you soon.
☐ E Yesterday we visited the Sagrada Familia and the Picasso Museum. In the evening we ate in a traditional Catalan restaurant.
  Greg & Anna

2 Match the headings below to the correct parts of the postcard in Exercise 1.

1 Future: say what you're going to do ☐
2 Greeting ☐
3 Past: say what you did ☐
4 Present: say where you are ☐
5 Sign off ☐

3 Meena is on holiday in Paris. It's Tuesday morning. Look at the documents and complete the postcard with the correct form of the verbs in brackets.

May
11 Monday
Visit the Louvre museum
Go up the Eiffel Tower

12 Tuesday
Write postcards
Take a boat trip on the River Seine

13 Wednesday

PARIS – Louvre

Dear Mum,
I <u>'m having</u> (have) a great time here in Paris. Paris [1] _____ (be) beautiful. Jacques' family [2] _____ (look) after me and his mum [3] _____ (give) me lots of great things to eat! At the moment, I [4] _____ (sit) in a café writing my postcard.
Yesterday, Jacques and I [5] _____ (go) to the Louvre and [6] _____ (see) the Mona Lisa. Then we [7] _____ (climb) to the top of the Eiffel Tower. The view [8] _____ (be) amazing!
This afternoon we [9] _____ (take) a boat trip on the River Seine and tomorrow morning I [10] _____ (relax) in the park.
See you soon!
Love
Meena

75

VOCABULARY AND GRAMMAR

1 Complete the sentences with names of clothes. The first letter of each word is given. (6 points)

That's a nice c<u>oat</u>. Now you have to find some nice b<u>oots</u> to go with it.

1 You can't wear a jacket and a s_____ without a t_____ .
2 Do you have to wear a s_____ to work? No, just a jacket and jeans are fine.
3 It's very cold today. You can't go outside without a warm s_____ .
4 The sun is very strong today. Take your s_____ with you.
5 You can't wear jeans. Put on some smarter t_____ .

2 Complete the sentences with the correct form of a phrasal verb. Use verbs and prepositions from the two boxes. (6 points)

put take (x2) ~~throw~~ try do pick
back on (x2) off ~~away~~ up (x2)

Please, don't <u>throw away</u> that magazine. I want to read it.

1 You don't have to _____ anything warm today. It's really hot so a T-shirt is enough.
2 What are these socks doing on the floor? _____ them _____ and put them in the washing machine.
3 I think I'm fatter than last year. I can't _____ this skirt.
4 _____ the headphones and listen to me for a while, please.
5 I like this dress but it's the wrong size. I'll have to _____ it _____ to the shop.
6 I often go shopping. I like _____ clothes _____ in the shop.

3 Complete the sentences with the correct forms of *going to* and the verbs in brackets. (5 points)

Jo <u>is going to visit</u> (visit) a local castle.

1 The campers _____ (play) tennis.
2 When _____ (they/go) on holiday this year?
3 Alex _____ (do) gymnastics every day.
4 _____ (he/fly) to London tonight?
5 I _____ (take) any smart clothes, just jeans and T-shirts.

4 Complete the sports camp holiday advertisement with *must, mustn't, don't have to, should* and *shouldn't*. (5 points)

SPORTS CAMP HOLIDAY

● You <u>must</u> organise the holiday before you arrive. We never have free places.

❶ You _____ do sports. It's your choice.

❷ You _____ smoke. The camp is a no-smoking area.

❸ You _____ eat well. It's a good idea and you need a lot of energy for the afternoon sessions.

❹ You _____ be too serious. The camp is for fun and playing is more important than winning.

❺ You _____ pay for anything here. Food and activities are all in the price of the holiday.

5 Complete the sentences with the correct forms of the verbs in brackets. Use the Present Simple or the Present Continuous. (8 points)

At the moment, I <u>'m trying</u> (try) to make a website.

1 _____ (Becky/work) today?
2 Where _____ (your friends/go) on Saturday nights?
3 I _____ (not buy) CDs, I download all my music from the Internet.
4 Hi, John, it's me, Mike. What _____ (you/do) at the moment?
5 Steve can't go swimming with us. He always _____ (play) tennis on Wednesdays.
6 We can't go to that club. We _____ (wear) jeans.
7 _____ (your sister/study) at university on Fridays?
8 Mum! Come here! John _____ (not do) his homework.

LISTENING SKILLS

6 **T44** Listen to the radio show about young people's clothes. Are the statements true (T), false (F) or is there no information (NI)? (7 points)

1 This week's show is about young people in the past. ☐
2 Mr Jessup's shop doesn't sell jeans. ☐
3 Joel is wearing a school uniform. ☐
4 Joel's got one suit. ☐
5 Joel's clothes tell us something about him. ☐
6 Joel has been to Mr Jessup's shop. ☐
7 Mr Jessup agrees that some T-shirts and trainers are stylish. ☐

COMMUNICATION

7 Complete the questions. The lines show how many words you need to use. (6 points)

Customer Good morning
Shop Assistant How <u>can</u> <u>I</u> <u>help</u>?

C I'm looking for a computer.
SA Well, we've got a lot of computers here.
C Mmm. Can you give me ¹_____ _____ about laptops?
SA Of course. They cost from £400 to £1500.
C Could ²_____ _____ _____ what the differences are?
SA Well, some have a bigger memory and are faster. Some can play DVDs.
C What do you ³_____ _____ 'faster'?
SA The computer works more quickly. It's important for playing games.
C Well, I'm not sure.
SA ⁴_____ _____ give you our brochure? It tells you all about the different computers.
C Thank you. Have you got a shop in Brighton?
SA Yes. I can ⁵_____ _____ the address if you like. Have you got a piece of paper?
C Yes.
SA Thirty-eight Station Road, Brighton.
C Sorry, ⁶_____ _____ _____ thirty-eight or forty-eight?
SA Thirty-eight.
C Right. Thanks very much.

READING SKILLS

8 Read the rules for the country of Freedownia and complete the sentences with one or two words. (7 points)

1 One thing that everyone who enters Freedownia needs is _____ .
2 People from the _____ do not need visas.
3 You can book hotel rooms at an office at the _____ .
4 To get the bus from the airport, you must have exactly twenty five _____ .
5 Only Freedownians can travel in _____ .
6 On Thursdays, women have to wear a hat but only in the _____ .
7 You can't eat _____ but you can have a picnic in the special picnic room.

Welcome to Freedownia

RULES FOR VISITORS

• All people coming into Freedownia must have a passport. People from the European Union don't have to have a visa. Everybody else must apply for a visa. When you arrive, you must have $500 or a credit card. You must change the money into Freedownian pounds at the Freedownia National Bank.

• You must also have somewhere to stay. You can book a room at our hotel finder office here at Freedownia airport. There are many beautiful hotels in the city. It is illegal to stay in campsites or in people's houses.

• There is a bus service from the airport to the city centre. It costs 25 Freedownia pence. You must have the correct money. The bus driver can't give you change. You mustn't use the black taxis. These are for Freedownians only. You can find tourist taxis, they are yellow and green, at the main airport entrance. The price to the city centre is 10 Freedownian pounds.

• We have some rules about clothes and places to eat. Men mustn't wear shorts or T-shirts on Sundays and women must wear a hat on Thursday afternoons. Nobody can eat outside. There are no ice creams or fast-food restaurants in Freedownia. You must eat in restaurants or you can have a picnic in our special city-centre picnic room.

• Have a nice time in Freedownia!

Total _____ /50

77

Body and mind

GRAMMAR

Present Perfect

We use the Present Perfect to talk about a past action and its result/situation now, e.g.
He **'s cleaned** the house. (= the house is clean now.)
He **hasn't cleaned** the house. (= the house is dirty now.)

	Affirmative	Negative
I/You/We/They	**have ('ve) cleaned** the house.	**have not (haven't) cleaned** the house.
He/She/It	**has ('s) cleaned** the house.	**has not (hasn't) cleaned** the house.

Yes/No questions			Short answers
Have	I/you/we/they	cleaned the house?	Yes, I/you/we/they **have**. No, I/you/we/they **haven't**.
Has	he/she/it		Yes, he/she/it **has**. No, he/she/it **hasn't**.

Wh- questions

How much work have you done?
Why haven't you cleaned the house?

Past Simple and Present Perfect

If we want to say exactly when something happened, we use the Past Simple:
*I **visited** China **when I was eighteen**.*

With the Present Perfect, we don't say exactly when something happened. It means 'at some point in the past up to now':
*I**'ve visited** China.*

Have you ever ...?

The adverb *ever* means 'at any time'. You can use it in questions.
A *Have you **ever** visited China?*
B *Yes, I have. I visited China when I was eighteen.*

---

1 Read the situations and complete the sentences and questions using the Present Perfect form of the words in brackets.

> Jack's not at home. He is shopping now.
> He's gone shopping. (go)

1 I can't find my glasses.
I _____ (lose) my glasses.
2 Is this new film with DiCaprio interesting?
I don't know, I _____ (not/see) it.
3 It's not raining now.
It _____ (stop) raining.
4 Is your homework ready?
_____ you _____ (finish) your homework?

2 Choose the correct phrases.

> *I* ⟨ate⟩ / *I've eaten* in an Italian restaurant yesterday.

1 Angie can't go out: *She didn't finish / She hasn't finished* her homework.
2 I'm exhausted. *I swam / I've swum* five kilometres.
3 *Did you see / Have you seen* Jackie at the weekend?
4 Happy Birthday! *We made / We've made* you a cake!
5 *Have you eaten / Did you eat* Japanese food?
6 Lisa and Claire *saw / have seen* Bruce Springsteen last year.

3 Complete the conversation with the correct forms of the words in brackets.

Sam Have you ever eaten Vietnamese food?
(eat/Vietnamese food)
Ethan Yes, I have (Yes/I). [1]_____ (I/eat) some last week.
Sam [2]_____ (you/like it)?
Ethan Yes, I did. [3]_____ (My mum/cook) it. She often cooks it.
[4]_____ (She/be) to Vietnam.
Sam Really? When [5]_____ (she/go) there?
Ethan [6]_____ (She/go) about ten years ago.
Sam Your parents are amazing. [7]_____ (They/both/do) some brilliant things in their lives. My parents [8]_____ (not/even/be) to France.
Ethan Why [9]_____ (you/ask) me about Vietnamese food?
Sam There's a new Vietnamese restaurant in town. I'm taking Sandra. She [10]_____ (not/try) Vietnamese food before. What's the best thing to order?
Ethan Try *Bo Kho*. [11]_____ (I/eat) it lots of times and it's delicious.

READING

1 Read the text. Match the pictures to the correct paragraphs.

1 _____

2 _____

3 _____

4 _____

5 _____

2 Read the text again. Put the sentences A–G into the correct places in the text (1–6). There is one extra sentence.

A I've shown them my photos of my holiday.
B I couldn't stop.
C I've tried jogging but I hated it.
D I've always wanted to be a pop star so I decided to enter.
E When I ate it, it was really hot.
F Last year we went to France.
G I don't enjoy singing at all.

3 T45 Listen and check your answers.

4 Find words in the text that match these definitions.

1 A small plate that you often put under a cup. _____

2 Numbers or letters that show how well or badly you are doing at school. _____

3 Something you wear when you go swimming. _____

4 What actors or singers stand on in the theatre or a concert. _____

5 A long thin green or red vegetable which is very spicy. _____

Be happy in body and mind.

Our readers' ideas

A I'm going on holiday to the beach this summer and I want to look good but I've eaten too much this year. The problem is I don't know the best way to do it. ¹____ It's so boring running through the streets before school. I've tried diets but people keep offering me food and I can't say 'No'. Now I know what to do. I've bought a bigger swimming costume!

> **MY TIP: Don't worry about things you can't change!**

B My parents love travelling so I've seen many nice places and done lots of interesting things. ²____ I wanted to go to the south but we didn't have time. We went to Paris. I've been there four times now and I love it. We finished by the sea near Mont St Michel. This year I'm going on holiday with some friends. ³____ Now they want to go there too.

> **MY TIP: If you enjoy something once, do it again!**

C I haven't visited many foreign countries, but last year I went to Budapest with my parents. I've eaten goulash in England and I like it so I wanted to try some real Hungarian goulash. It came in a bowl with a small saucer of chilli. I've eaten spicy food before so I put all the chilli into my goulash. Big mistake! ⁴____ I drank about two litres of water but it was great. I ate it again the next day!

> **MY TIP: Be brave and see what happens. You might like it!**

D For my birthday, my parents gave me a football manager computer game. I didn't like it at first because it was very complicated. Then I started to understand how to play it. ⁵____ I played it all the time.

I stopped playing sports and my school marks got worse and worse. I stayed up late every night and, in the end, my parents threw the game away and bought me some new skis. I feel much better now.

> **MY TIP: Don't let anything take over your life!**

E Last month, our school had a singing competition. ⁶____ I chose the Michael Jackson song, *Billie Jean*. I spent ages looking at his videos and finally knew how to do the 'moon walk', his special dance. I started to dream about being a star, playing in concerts with people screaming my name. What happened? I got on stage, I tried the walk and... I fell over. Everyone laughed and I couldn't continue. I didn't win!

> **MY TIP: Don't try to be something you aren't!**

GRAMMAR

Present Perfect with *just*, *already* and *yet*

We use *just*, *already* and *yet* to add extra meaning to the Present Perfect. We use *just* and *already* in affirmative sentences. Use them between *have* and the verb:

A *You look different.*
B *I've **just** had a haircut. (**just** means very recently, a short time ago.)*

A *Do your homework!*
B *I've **already** done it. (**already** means faster or sooner than expected.)*

We use *yet* in negative sentences and questions. Use it at the end of the sentence:

A *What are you doing?*
B *I'm writing letters. I haven't finished **yet**. I've got two more to write.*

A *Have you seen the new Spielberg film **yet**?*
B *No, we haven't. But we're going to see it at the weekend. (**yet** means it is expected or it is going to happen.)*

Mind the trap!

Present Perfect with *been* and *gone*:

John's gone to Moscow. (= He's in Moscow now. He's not here.)

John's been to Moscow. (= He's not in Moscow now. He visited Moscow at some time in the past.)

1 Complete the conversations with *been* or *gone*.

A Hello Mrs Sanchez. Can I speak to Julio?
B I'm afraid he's not here. He's <u>gone</u> out.

1 A You look tired.
B Yes. I've _____ to the gym.

2 A Where's Maureen?
B She's _____ to the shop for some milk.

3 A Let's go to the art gallery.
B I don't want to. I've _____ there. It was boring.

4 A You look great.
B Thank you. I've _____ on holiday.

5 A Where have you _____ ?
B I've _____ at my yoga class. Why?
A Pete came to see you. He waited for ages. He's _____ now.

2 Look at the pictures and write sentences. Use the Present Perfect form of the phrases in the box with *just*.

arrive   get married   have an accident
~~have a baby~~   finish lunch
pass her driving test

They've just had a baby.

1 _____

2 _____

3 _____

4 _____

5 _____

3 Penny is a journalist. It's only 10 a.m. but she's already done a lot of things. Write sentences with *already* and *yet*.

TO DO
Finish writing the 'Celebrity Diets' article ✓
Phone Tom
1 Read the newspapers
2 Listen to Jay-Z's new CD ✓
3 Write the article about Jay-Z
4 Email Brad ✓

She's already finished writing the 'Celebrity Diets' article.
She hasn't phoned Tom yet.

1 _____
2 _____
3 _____
4 _____

LISTENING

1 [T46] You are going to listen to a radio programme about hosting the World Cup in Australia. Before you listen, try to predict whether the following are advantages (A) or disadvantages (D). Then listen to check.

good stadiums ☐A

1 good transport systems (trains, buses, roads) ☐
2 big country ☐
3 a long way from other countries ☐
4 cool weather ☐
5 football is not a very popular sport there ☐
6 different time zones from Europe ☐
7 safe country ☐

2 [T46] Listen again. Complete the sentences with one word in each space.

Australia has held the Olympics *twice*.

1 It is winter in Australia in _____ .
2 People can enjoy themselves on the _____ .
3 Perth to Sydney is about the same distance as _____ to _____ .
4 Matches have to start at _____ .
5 Australia have played in the last _____ World Cups.
6 The Australians know how to _____ .

SPEAKING

1 [T47] Complete the general description of the picture with words from the box. Then listen and check.

a because can can't I in It's it's left Maybe think of picture see

1 It's _____ _____ _____ a street.
2 I _____ _____ _____ the UK _____ they are driving on the _____ .
3 _____ _____ _____ seven people.
4 I _____ see anyone wearing a coat. _____ it's the summer.

2 [T48] Choose the correct answers in the detailed description of the picture. Then listen and check.

There are two cars *on the left /* *on the right*. [1] *They've just had / They're having* an accident. The drivers [2] *look / look like* very angry. There's a man on a bicycle [3] *in the middle / on the right* of the road. [4] *He's looking / He's looked* at a girl in the street. I think [5] *she's buying / she's just bought* a new dress. [6] *She's showing / She's shown* it to her friend. They both [7] *look / look like* happy. [8] *On the left / On the right*, there's a couple in a café. [9] *They're having / They've just had* lunch. [10] *They're watching / They're going to watch* the man on the bicycle. I think [11] *he's had / he's going to have* an accident, too.

WORD LIST

Sports
athletics
baseball
baseball bat
basketball
break the world record
canoeing
champion
cheering
cycling
diving
goalkeeper
gymnastics
high jump
hockey
jogging
jump (v)
kick-off
match (n)
(gold) medal
(gold) medallist
Olympic Games
pitch
race (n)
rock climbing
run (v)
runner
sailing
skiing
sports event
sports facilities
sportsman
supporter
table tennis
tennis
throw
track
volleyball
winner

Other
aeroplane
against
already
beat
begin
billion
blanket
body

call (v)
carry
check your emails
clean your teeth
come out
concentrate
cool box
count (v)
dash
day out
far (adv)
fight (n)
find
fizzy drink
frightening
impossible
join a gym
just
kangaroo
leaflet
letter
long way away
magnificent
maximum
mind (n)
mind-boggling
mineral water
natural
neuron
plan (v)
power (n)
put
regular
report (v)
right-handed
routine
score a goal/a point
second (n)
speed reader
straightforward
struggle (n)
though
typical
unaided
unusual
vitamin pills
well (adj)
yet

VOCABULARY

1 Complete the sporting activities.

a t h l e t i c s

1 b ___ s ___ b ___ ___ ___
2 b ___ s ___ ___ t ___ ___ ___ ___
3 c ___ n ___ e ___ ___ ___
4 c ___ c ___ ___ ___ g
5 d ___ v ___ ___ ___
6 g ___ m ___ ___ s ___ ___ c ___
7 h ___ c ___ e ___
8 j ___ g ___ ___ ___ ___
9 s ___ ___ l ___ ___ ___
10 s ___ i i ___ ___
11 t ___ b ___ ___ t ___ n ___ ___ ___
12 t ___ n ___ ___ ___
13 v ___ ___ l ___ y ___ ___ ___ l

2 Match the words to the correct pictures.

~~goalkeeper~~ medallist runner sportsman supporter winner

goalkeeper

1 _____

2 _____

3 _____

4 _____   5 _____

3 Match the pairs of words.

Olympic	c	**a** box
1 baseball	☐	**b** pills
2 gold	☐	**c** ~~Games~~
3 sports	☐	**d** drink
4 vitamin	☐	**e** facilities
5 rock	☐	**f** medal
6 fizzy	☐	**g** climbing
7 cool	☐	**h** bat

4 Choose the correct answers.

Remember to [clean] / *comb* / *cool* your teeth three times a day after meals.

1 Sorry I didn't reply earlier but I haven't *looked* / *checked* / *made* my emails for a few days.

2 If I *score* / *beat* / *win* the race, I'll get the gold medal!

3 If you want to lose weight, you should *keep* / *follow* / *join* a gym.

4 You have to finish in 9.76 seconds if you want to *break* / *win* / *score* the world record.

5 I'm not sure that we can *beat* / *win* / *lose* this team – they're very good.

6 Torres *beat* / *scored* / *won* a goal and Spain won 1–0.

5 Complete the descriptions with words from the box.

champion   cheered   dashed   ~~frightening~~
impossible   kick off   mind-boggling   pitch
track   unaided

A

It was <u>frightening</u> for the players when the crowd ran onto the ¹_____ before the match. It was three o'clock but they couldn't ²_____ until the police moved everyone out of the way.

B

The man was tied up with rope, locked in a box and put at the bottom of the lake. He had three minutes to get out ³_____ . Surely it was ⁴_____ . Suddenly, he appeared alive and well. How did he do it? It was a ⁵_____ trick.

C

As the runners ran round the ⁶_____ for the last time, the crowd ⁷_____ more loudly. Suddenly, the Kenyan ⁸_____ forward and went past the other runners. He smiled as he crossed the line. He was the new world ⁹_____ .

WRITING | Personal letter

1 Read the letter. Pay no attention to the gaps. Match the headings to the correct boxes.

Closing   Date   ~~Greeting~~   Sign off   News 1
Your name   News 2   Opening

1 _____

| Greeting |

27 November

2 _____

Dear Helen,

<u>How nice</u> to get your letter. ¹_____ you're enjoying Seville - it's a beautiful city. Perhaps I should come and visit you next year. ²_____ I haven't written for so long. ³_____ very busy at work.

⁴_____ some good news. ⁵_____ my driving test and my dad's bought me a car. It's a Red VW Golf and ⁶_____ . ⁷_____ drive up to Edinburgh in it next week to see Nick. I'm a bit nervous because ⁸_____ very much on my own yet.

3 _____

I ⁹_____ bad news, though. Sandy, my cat, died last week. She was old for a cat - fifteen - but I'm still a bit sad about it. ¹⁰_____ her when I was ten years old so she was a part of the family for a long time. ¹¹_____ get another pet. Not for a few years, anyway.

4 _____

¹²_____ you? ¹³_____ be in the UK for Christmas? ¹⁴_____ and tell me all your news from Seville.

Love,

Lucy.

5 _____

7 _____

6 _____

2 Read the letter again. Complete gaps 1–14 with phrases from the box.

Are you going to	~~How nice~~
I got	I haven't driven
have some	I love it
I'm glad	I'm going to
I'm not going to	I'm sorry
I've been	I've passed
Please write soon	What about
I've got	

83

 # Look to the future

GRAMMAR

will

We use *will* to talk about the future:
*Tomorrow it **will** rain.*

We use *will* to make predictions and state facts:
*There **will** always be wars.*
*Next year **will** be 2015.*

	Affirmative	Negative
I/You/He/She/It/We/They	**will ('ll) get** married.	**will not (won't) get** married.

Yes/No questions			Short answers
Will	I/you/he/she/it/we/they	**get** married?	Yes, I you/he/she/it/we/they **will**. No, I you/he/she/it/we/they **won't**.

Wh- questions
Where will you be?
When will you be there?
What will you do there?
How will you do that?

Language used with *will*

You can use 'extra' language with *will* to show how sure you are:

I'm sure I think I don't think	Anne **will** pass her Maths exam.

Mind the trap!

We do not use *to* after *will*:
I will get married.
(NOT ~~I will to get married.~~)

1 Complete the sentences with *will* or *won't*.

Don't worry: the exam <u>won't</u> be difficult.

1 The film starts at 8 p.m. so I _____ meet you at the cinema at 7.45.

2 Friday is a holiday: there _____ be any lessons.

3 Who do you think _____ win? Real Madrid or Zenit St Petersburg?

4 Jack's gone home, but he _____ be back tomorrow.

5 They have to go to Paris for a meeting tomorrow so they _____ be in the office.

6 I _____ be ready in a minute – I just have to find my keys.

7 _____ you be at home on Tuesday evening?

8 Don't have another coffee – you _____ sleep.

9 She's never travelled alone before: do you think she _____ be alright?

10 I am sure Mark _____ come on time.

2 Complete the sentences with *will* and verbs from the box.

be (x 2)   drive   go   have   ~~live~~   make   speak   study

In the future, people <u>will live</u> for 200 years.

1 In ten years, many people _____ small computers inside their bodies.

2 In 2020, most children won't go to school; they _____ at home.

3 Ten years from now, everyone _____ electric cars.

4 One day, everybody in the world _____ English.

5 Soon, computers _____ more intelligent than the average person.

6 By 2025, most people in my country _____ to work by private plane.

7 By 2030, China _____ the richest country in the world.

8 By 2035, computers _____ important political decisions for us.

3 Look at the pictures and make sentences with *will* or *won't*.

It / rain tomorrow
It will rain tomorrow.

1 Tomorrow / be Wednesday

_____

2 I / be eighteen / next year

_____

3 You / be tired / tomorrow

_____
_____

4 We / get the tickets

_____
_____

4 Put the questions 1–4 in the correct order and match them to the answers a–e.

rain / will / tomorrow / it
Will it rain tomorrow? ⓒ

1 Mr Jones / will / Friday / us / homework / give / on

_____ ☐

2 buy / your / will / a motorbike / parents / you

_____ ☐

3 ever / you / get / will / married

_____ ☐

4 at / sister / you / be / party / Erin's / and your / will

_____ ☐

a Yes, we will.   **d** Yes, he will.
b No, they won't.   **e** No, I won't.
c ~~No, it won't.~~

5 Complete the conversation with the correct forms of the words in brackets. Use *will* and *won't*.

Mia Hurry up or <u>you will be</u> (you/be) late.
Josh Late for what?
Mia Lisa. ¹_____ (she/be) here soon. You should go to the station to meet her.
Josh She hasn't phoned yet. ²_____ (she/ring) when the train gets here.
Mia How long ³_____ (it/take) you to get to the station?
Josh About fifteen minutes.
Mia I think you should go now. ⁴_____ (the café/be) closed, and ⁵_____ (there/not be) anywhere for her to wait.
Josh ⁶_____ (she/have) her dog with her?
Mia ⁷_____ (Yes/she). She always takes her dog on holiday with her.
Josh The bus driver ⁸_____ (not/let us) on with a dog.
Mia Get a taxi.
Josh A taxi! How much ⁹_____ (that/cost)?
Mia About £5. But don't worry, ¹⁰_____ (I/give) you the money.
Josh ¹¹_____ (you/give) me the money for a taxi to the station?
Mia ¹²_____ (No/I). You can walk!

6 Rewrite the sentences using the words in brackets.

She will fail the exam.
I don't think she'll pass the exam. (don't think/pass)
Jane will come on time.
I'm sure Jane will come on time. (sure)

1 John will be on time.

_____ (sure)

2 The story will have a happy ending.

_____ (think)

3 The exam will be difficult.

_____ (don't think/easy)

4 The weather will get better next week.

_____ (sure)

5 The sea will be warm.

_____ (don't think/cold)

READING

1 T49 Read and listen to four people's fears for the future. Match the texts to the pictures.

1 ☐

This is a big problem at the moment. Although governments are trying to clean up lakes and rivers, air pollution is bad, especially in big cities because of traffic jams. I think that scientists will find new forms of clean energy. They have to because the old 'dirty' energy: oil, gas and coal, will run out. We'll use wind power for electricity and water for cars. The problem is that many countries are becoming more industrial with more cars and factories so there will be more pollution in the near future and then the world will get cleaner.

2 ☐

This is a problem now in many parts of the world. There are too many people and soon there won't be anywhere for wild animals to live. People will cut down rainforests for the wood or to make more room for farms. More people will be hungry and will hunt wild animals. It doesn't matter if they are protected. People will be desperate. I think many more animals will become extinct and the problem will get worse and worse. The only place we will be able to see them is the zoo.

3 ☐

In my country, there's litter everywhere. In the countryside and National Parks, which people visit because of their beauty, you can see people throwing rubbish on the ground. The fields near my home are full of rubbish. Even the ground next to the recycling bins is covered in paper! I don't know why. People in other countries don't do this. Children at school learn about the problem so I hope the next generation will be better.

4 ☐

I'm worried about the problem of feeding everyone in the world. The population is growing every year. I know scientists have created GM* plants which grow even when the weather is bad or there is no rain, but these worry me too. Some people say they are great and will produce more food than we need, others say that they kill bees and other important insects and might not grow in a few years. Who should I believe? I have no idea.

*GM = Genetically modified

2 Read the texts again and match the headings to the correct paragraphs. There is one extra heading.

A It's very bad now but not in every country. ☐

B It will get much worse. ☐

C There isn't a problem now but there will be. ☐

D It will get worse before it gets better. ☐

E I don't know what will happen. ☐

3 Choose the correct answers.

1 The world will be cleaner in the future because
  a there won't be any dirty energy.
  b it will be windier.
  c there won't be so much traffic.
  d poorer countries won't need so much energy.

2 Which of these is not a reason for animals becoming extinct?
  a People eating them.
  b Animals losing their homes.
  c People taking animals to zoos.
  d Too many people in the world.

3 The only place where there is no rubbish is
  a by recycling bins.
  b in other countries.
  c in National Parks.
  d near the writer's home.

4 The writer doesn't know if
  a there will be more people in the world.
  b people will grow GM crops.
  c GM crops will be a good or bad thing.
  d there will be any rain in the future.

GRAMMAR

Adverbs of manner

Adverbs of manner tell us how something is done:
You walk **quickly**.
He smiled **happily**.
She's done her work **well**.

Adverbs usually go at the end of a phrase.

To make adverbs from most adjectives, add **-ly**:
quick → quick**ly**, natural → natural**ly**

For adjectives ending in -y, change -y to **-ily**:
easy → eas**ily**, happy → happ**ily**

Good is irregular:
good → **well**

Mind the trap!

Some adverbs have the same form as adjectives:

early → **early**   fast → **fast**
hard → **hard**   late → **late**

1 Complete the sentences with the adverbs formed from the adjectives in the box.

bad   careful   fast   good   hard   ~~slow~~   quick

My English isn't very good: please, speak <u>slowly</u>.

1 I'm only going to say this once so please listen _____ .

2 It's an emergency: come _____ !

3 It's an interesting job, but you'll have to work _____ .

4 Dinner was wonderful: you cook so _____ .

5 She's very athletic – she can run very _____ .

6 I'm taking piano lessons because I play very _____ .

2 Complete the sentences with the correct answers.

silent / silently
The class did the exam <u>silently</u>.
The class were <u>silent</u> during the exam.

1 *good / well*
Marco's speaking skills are _____ .
Marco speaks English _____ .

2 *slow / slowly*
Why do you walk so _____ ?
Why are you so _____ ?

3 *excited / excitedly*
The students talked about their holidays _____ .
The students were _____ about their holidays.

4 *angry / angrily*
My dad was _____ and shouted 'Be quiet!'
'Be quiet!' shouted my dad _____ .

5 *easy / easily*
Arsenal won the match _____ .
It was an _____ win for Arsenal.

SPEAKING

1 Match the people 1–4 to the opinions A–D.

> **In my opinion, we should all be vegetarians.**

A Yes, I completely agree.

B I'm afraid I disagree.

> **We should cycle to school.**

C I know what you mean but I disagree.

D You are absolutely right!

1 Someone who is fit and energetic. ☐
2 Someone who hates meat. ☐
3 Someone who cares about the environment but lives a long way away from school. ☐
4 Someone whose favourite meal is burger and chips. ☐

2 **T50** Complete the conversations with words from the box. Then listen to check.

agree   completely   idea   mean   ~~personally~~   right   true

1
Tom   <u>Personally</u>, I think they should ban smoking in public places.
Anna   I'm sorry but I don't ¹_____ . Public places are for everybody.
Tom   That's ²_____ , but if I'm in a public place, why should I have to breathe your smoke?

2
Ellie   I don't think supermarkets should use plastic bags.
Sam   I know what you ³_____ , but people need something to put their shopping in.
Ellie   Well, then the customers should pay for them.
Sam   That's a good ⁴_____ .

3
Natalie I think that the police should do more to stop people dropping litter.
Jeremy You are absolutely ⁵_____ . It's disgusting.
Natalie: Anyone who drops one piece of litter should pay a fine.
Jeremy I ⁶_____ agree.

87

WORD LIST

The environment
air
clean energy
climate change
countryside
cut down
cycle lane
degree (Celsius)
die out
disappear
electricity
endangered
extinction
food shortage
forest
glass
green
litter
mountains
natural world
ocean
oxygen
packaging
paper
petrol
planet
plant (n, v)
plastic bag
pollute
pollution
produce
protect
public transport
rainforest
recycle
recycling bin
recycling scheme
resources
rubbish
save
sea
species
temperature
throw away
traffic jam
tree
waste (v)
wind (n)
world population

Animals
cheetah
cow
crocodile
dog
dolphin
donkey
elephant
koala
lion
monkey
panda
penguin
pig
sheep
tiger
whale

Other
absolutely
act (v)
around
article

badly
balcony
ban
bark
bath
build
car park
change (n)
climb
close (to sth) (adj)
complain
completely
damage (v)
dangerously
definite
definitely
developed world
difference
dramatic
dramatically
drop
easily
edition
elegantly
empty
exist
farm animals
generous
generously
go up (by)
grow (v)
happily
hard (adv)
human
increase (v)
law
lose
loudly
machine
madam
make sure
noisily
on stand-by
overnight
past (n)
post (n)
quietly
reduce
resident
roar (v)
sb is running out of sth
second-hand
shopper
shopping centre
site
steel
style (n)
support (v)
survive
swap
switch off/on
thousand
tonne
town/city council
true
type (v)
under
unfashionable
unnecessary
unwanted
urgent
urgently
via
wash (v)
wild animals
window box

88

VOCABULARY

1 Complete the names of the animals.

crocodile

1 l_____

2 d_____

3 p_____

4 e_____

5 c_____

6 m_____

7 p_____

8 d_____

9 w_____

2 Match the words to make collocations.

clean	d	**a** lane
1 climate	☐	**b** animals
2 cycle	☐	**c** world
3 food	☐	**d** ~~energy~~
4 natural	☐	**e** bin
5 public	☐	**f** change
6 recycling	☐	**g** world
7 developed	☐	**h** transport
8 wild	☐	**i** shortage

3 Make phrasal verbs from the words in the box. Then complete the sentences with the correct forms of the verbs.

away   cut   ~~die~~   down   go   off   on   ~~out~~   switch (x2)   throw   up

Dinosaurs <u>died</u> <u>out</u> 65 million years ago.

1 The climate is changing: temperatures are _____ _____ every year.

2 Remember to _____ the computer _____ when you finish work.

3 When I was a child, this was a beautiful place, but last year they _____ _____ all the trees.

4 How much electricity do I use when I _____ _____ the TV?

5 Don't _____ bottles and cans _____ – recycle them.

4 Complete the sentences with the correct forms of the words in capitals.

I <u>completely</u> (COMPLETE) agree with you.

1 We should do what we can to save _____ (DANGER) animals.
2 What's the _____ (DIFFERENT) between *pollution* and *rubbish*?
3 My older brother very _____ (GENEROUS) gave me £100 when I started university.
4 My dad's old clothes are really _____ (FASHION) and old.
5 Can you look after an _____ (WANT) cat?
6 All the rubbish _____ (APPEAR) overnight and no-one knows where it went.
7 Don't waste _____ (ELECTRIC).
8 The _____ (SHORT) of land for animals in many countries is very worrying.

5 Complete the texts with one word in each gap. The first letter of each word is given.

A

I don't drive to work now. They have built a <u>cycle lane</u> so I go by bike. It's a great feeling to go straight past all the cars in a ¹ t_____ j_____ . It's good for the ² e_____ and I also ³ s_____ a lot of money because I don't have to buy ⁴ p_____ for my car.

B

The trees in the ⁵ f_____ and ⁶ r_____ provide the ⁷ p_____ Earth with the ⁸ o_____ we need to live. Now we are cutting them down faster than they can ⁹ g_____ . What will happen to us when the trees have gone?

C

Many ¹⁰ e_____ animals will become ¹¹ e_____ in the next fifty years. We need to act quickly to ¹² p_____ them.

6 Replace the words in brackets with the correct forms of the verbs in the box.

~~act~~ ban complain drop grow rise roar support

Tigers are in danger. We have to (*do something*) <u>act</u> now to help them.

1 The government has (*stopped people from*) _____ smoking at work.
2 The Earth's temperature is (*going up*) _____ every year.
3 Don't (*throw*) _____ your litter on the floor.
4 My mother (*told the waiter*) _____ that her soup was cold.
5 The best thing about the safari was waking up to hear the lions (*making the noise that lions make*) _____ .
6 I (*agree with*) _____ Greenpeace.
7 Some trees (*get bigger*) _____ more quickly than others so are good for paper making.

WRITING | Formal letter

1 Read the letter and answer the questions 1–7.

15 May 2011

Dear Ms Ritchie,

I am writing to complain about the television programme Rainforest Rip Off, which was produced by your company.

In the programme you made a number of incorrect statements about my organisation, The Amazon Group. For example, you said that we received money from the Brazilian government, which is not true.

We do a lot of work to help save the rainforest and your programme might mean that people will stop giving us money. This could have a terrible effect both locally and for the whole planet.

I feel very strongly about this and I would like to meet you at your London offices to discuss what can be done now.

Yours,

John B Waterman

Director

1 Is the letter *formal* or *informal*?
2 Did the author know the name of the person he wrote to? *yes / no*
3 Who is the author of the letter? *Ms Ritchie / John Waterman*
4 What word can you add to the sign-off? *faithfully / sincerely*
5 Why did the writer write the letter? *to thank someone / to complain about something*
6 Can you use short forms like *I'm* or *I'd like* in a formal letter? *yes / no*
7 What phrase can you use if you don't know the name of the person you write to? *Dear Sir or Madam / Dear Ms or Mr*

2 Read the reply to the letter in Exercise 1. Look at the highlighted phrases and decide which of them are correct and which are incorrect in a formal letter.

23 may 2011

¹Hi, John

²I'm writing in reply to your letter. ³I'll be glad to meet you. My secretary, Eva Jackson, ⁴will contact you to arrange a time. ⁵Could you please send us your telephone number so that she can discuss this with ⁶you?

Our aim was to find the truth about your organisation but, if we have made some mistakes, ⁷we'll try to put them right ⁸as soon as possible!

⁹Bye

Isabella Ritchie

¹⁰Managing director

VOCABULARY AND GRAMMAR

1 Write the name of the sport next to each
description. (5 points)

People do this in the mountains. It looks
dangerous but if you are careful, you don't
fall. <u>rock climbing</u>

1 This is a winter sport. Going down the
mountain is very exciting. _____

2 Different sports belong to this category, like
running, jumping and throwing. _____

3 This is a good sport in the gym or on the
beach. You just need a net and a ball. _____

4 You do it on a lake or at sea. You need a boat
or a yacht for it. _____

5 There are two types of this sport. The game
on ice is faster and very popular in the USA
or Canada. In England the game on grass is
more popular. _____

2 Complete the sentences with the correct verbs.
The first letter of each verb is given. (6 points)

It's easy to s<u>ave </u>paper. Just print on both
sides.

1 Don't throw those bottles away. We can
r_____ them.

2 Our government should p_____ more
trees.

3 Go to school by bicycle. Cars p_____ the
air.

4 He'll eat that piece of pizza. He never
w_____ food.

5 Don't forget to c_____ your teeth after
breakfast.

6 He ran fast but he didn't b_____ the
world record.

3 Complete the sentences with the correct forms of
words from the box. (5 points)

beautiful	good	quick	dangerous
easy	~~bad~~		

He is a hopeless driver. He really drives
<u>badly.</u>

1 Alan is very good at football. He plays it
very _____ .

2 Do you think that dog is _____ ?

3 I can't understand my teacher. He talks
very _____ .

4 It's not really difficult. You can do
it _____ .

5 Why didn't Susan Boyle win *Britain's Got
Talent*? She sings _____ .

4 Complete the sentences and questions below.
Use *will*, *won't* and the words in brackets. (4 points)

In the future, <u>everybody will speak</u>
(everybody/speak) English.

1 I think _____ (Josh/win) this match, his
opponent is much better.

2 What _____ (the weather/be) on Sunday?

3 _____ (people/use) petrol in 2040?

4 I am sure _____ (you/have) any problems
with this exercise, it isn't very difficult.

5 Choose the correct words. (4 points)

Have you (ever) / *yet* been to the Olympic
Games?

1 I only arrived here two days ago but I've
already / just been on three excursions.

2 **A** Are you going on holiday this summer?
B Well, I've *yet / just* come back from my
holidays so my next holiday will be in the
winter.

3 Are you still ill? Have you been to the doctor's
ever / yet?

4 I've played a lot of games of football but I've
never / ever scored a goal.

6 Complete the sentences. Use the Past Simple
or the Present Perfect form of the verbs in brackets.
(6 points)

I <u>'ve been </u>(go) to the USA three times.

1 _____ (you/see) the new film at the
cinema? You should, it's great.

2 That's a nice jacket. Where _____ (you/
buy) it?

3 Another win for Jerry. He _____ (already/
beat) five people in this competition.

4 The match last night was great.
We _____ (win) 66–38.

5 Oh no! We've got Maths today and
I _____ (not do) my homework.

6 I _____ (not go) anywhere last summer –
it was great!

LISTENING SKILLS

7 [T51] Listen to two people talking about a football match and complete the sentences with one or two words. (6 points)

1 The _____ at half time is 3–1 to Manchester Town.
2 Jack Sinclair is the manager of _____ .
3 This is Liverpool's third game in _____ .
4 Jack Sinclair thinks that the Liverpool manager should change _____ .
5 In fifty matches for Liverpool, Fletcher has scored _____ .
6 Fletcher isn't English, he's from _____ .

READING SKILLS

8 Read the advertisement for the National Trust and give short answers (maximum three words) to the questions 1–8. (8 points)

1 What does the National Trust look after in the UK?
_____

2 What does it teach people to do?
_____

3 According to the farming programme, who should we buy food from?
_____

4 How long will the National Trust protect its buildings?
_____

5 When did the National Trust start?
_____

6 How many members are there?
_____

7 How much do members have to pay to visit National Trust buildings?
_____

8 What do you need to sleep in if you want to go on a working holiday?
_____

COMMUNICATION

9 Match the sentence halves. (6 points)

In my opinion,	a
1 Yes, you're	☐
2 Personally, I don't think	☐
3 What I like about it	☐
4 I'm afraid	☐
5 It's the	☐
6 That's true	☐

a London is the best city in Europe.
b it will make any difference.
c but I still don't think it's a good idea.
d most fascinating city I've been to.
e it's also very polluted.
f is the history and excitement.
g absolutely right.

🍃 THE NATIONAL TRUST

The National Trust is an organisation which looks after buildings and countryside in most of the United Kingdom. It is Europe's biggest conservation charity and also tries to teach people how they can help the environment. As an example, their farming programme tries to get people to buy food from local farmers, not supermarkets.

Most of the buildings that the National Trust owns are open to the public and we will protect them forever. Nobody can destroy the National Trust buildings or build on its land. It started in 1895 and now has over three million members. The Trust needs members to get more money to help save Britain's nature and history.

Why be a member? Members get free entry to all National Trust buildings and we will send you our magazine to tell you all about our latest projects. You can also go on a National Trust working holiday. On one of our holidays, you sleep in the building which you are helping to clean. We give you all your meals and our group leaders will organise evening activities. All you need to bring are some old clothes, strong boots and a sleeping bag.

With your help, Britain can be a cleaner, more interesting and better protected place. Join us today.

Total _____ /50

91

Exam Vocabulary

People

Personal information

address
be called
come from
contact details
date of birth
(email) address
first name
form
full name
home city
ID card
language
live
male/female
marital status
married
name
nationality
phone no/number
sex
single
speak
surname

Age

aged
baby
boy
girl
I'm 18 years old.
man/men
middle-aged
old
people
person
teenager
woman/women
young

Appearance

face/body
bald
black
blonde
blue
curly
dark

fair
green
grey
hair
(light) brown
long
make-up
medium-length hair
round
short
soft
straight
wavy

Size

fat
short
slim
small
tall
thin

Opinion

attractive
beautiful
elegant
good-looking
look
lovely
pretty
ugly

Clothes and accessories

baseball cap
(blue) jeans
boots
button
casual clothes
coat
comb
dress
gloves
hat
jacket
shirt
shoes
shorts
skirt
suit
sunglasses
sweater

sweatshirt
T-shirt
tie
trainers
trousers
watch

Personality

active
adventurous
ambitious
boring
character
clever
confident
easy-going
energetic
friendly
funny
generous
good at
hard-working
intelligent
irresponsible
kind
lazy
lively
musical
nervous
nice
organised
quiet
relaxed
romantic
sensible
serious
shy
strange
stupid
talented

Feelings and emotions

anxious
be afraid (of sth)
bored
busy
desperate
excited
happy
lonely
mad
mood

pleased
sad
sleepy
stressed
sure
surprised
tired
worried

Home

Types of houses

block of flats
bungalow
cottage
detached house
flat/apartment
high-rise building
semi-detached house
terraced house

Parts of a house

attic
balcony
bathroom
bedroom
dining room
garage
garden
hall
kitchen
living room
room
shower
stairs
study
(thatched) roof
toilet
window
yard

Furniture and equipment

armchair
basin
bath
bed
blanket
chair
computer
cooker
cupboard
desk

dishwasher
door
drawer
DVD player
electricity
fitted kitchen
floor
flower
fridge
furnished
furniture
knife/knives
microwave (oven)
picture
plant
printer
radio
remote control
shelf/shelves
shower
sink
sofa
table
television
wall
wardrobe
washing machine
window box

Looking for accommodation/ Describing location

available
bill
building
convenient
cosy
downstairs
flatmate/roommate
for/to rent
housewarming party
ideal
live next door
modern
move
noise
noisy
owner
peaceful
per week/month
private
resident
share a flat

School

School and university subjects

Algebra
Art
Biology
Calculus
Chemistry
Economics
French
Geography
Geometry
History
Information Technology (IT)
Languages
Literature
Maths/Mathematics
Music
Physical Education (PE)
Physics
Spanish
Trigonometry

People

beginner
classmate
genius
lecturer
pupil
student
teacher
university

Places

classroom
college
department
language school
library
mixed school
primary school
school hall
secondary school
student hall
summer school
university

Learning, homework and exams

board
certificate
challenge
class
degree
dictionary
difficult
education
elementary
enrol
essay
exam
exam paper
exchange programme
fail an exam
gap year
grade
graduation
knowledge
late
leave school
lesson
mistake
notebook
pass an exam
pen
pencil
practise (v)
punish
read
school book/textbook
schoolwork
study
take an exam
teach
term
test
timetable
understand
uniform
write

Work

Jobs

actor/actress
artist
author
babysitter
builder
bus driver
cake decorator
chef
chocolate maker
computer programmer
cook
dentist
doctor
engineer
farmer
fire-fighter
gardener
hairdresser
ice-cream tester
lifeguard
nurse
operator
pilot
police officer
postman/postwoman
receptionist
referee
reporter
secretary
shop assistant
soldier
taxi driver
teacher
university professor
vet
waiter/waitress
window cleaner

Looking for a job

achievement
application form
be good with children/people/
    money/animals/computers
be prepared
body language
current employment
CV
director
driving licence
formal clothes
job interview
letter of application
passion
unemployed
voluntary work
well-paid
work experience

At work

arrive on time
boss
calendar
career
company
conference
earn
employer
full-time
money
office
pay
part-time
pick fruit
skills
special qualifications/equipment
staff
type
wear special clothes/a uniform/
    boots
website design
work hard
work long hours/inside/outside/
    at weekends/at night/late/in a
    team/on your own/in an office

Family and social life

Family and friends

aunt
boyfriend
brother
children
cousin
daughter
family
family tree
father/dad
friend
girlfriend
grandchildren
grandfather
grandmother
grandparents
grandson
husband
kid
madam
mother/mum
nephew
niece

parents
pen friend
sir
sister
son
stepfather
stepmother
uncle
wife

Everyday activities

alarm
be asleep
clean up
clean your teeth
cut the grass
daily routine
forget
get dressed
get up
get/go home
go
go out
go to bed
have a break
have a coffee
have a drink
have a shower/bath
have breakfast/lunch/dinner
help
housework
listen (to)
shave
sleep
usual
wake (up)
walk (n)
walk (v)
walk the dog
wash
wash up
watch

Months

January
February
March
April
May
June
July
August
September
October
November
December

Days of the week

Monday
Tuesday
Wednesday
Thursday
Friday
Saturday
Sunday

Time expressions

after (school)
always
at 8 o'clock
at night
at the weekend
before
date
every (morning)
how often
in January/2011
in the morning/afternoon/
    evening
in the summer
never
often
on 31 August
on Monday/Sunday night
sometimes
usually
what time
when

Socialising, holidays and celebrations

advice (n)
answer the phone
apologise
appointment
argument
ask (for)
barbecue
be no good (at)
birthday
birthday cake
(bon)fire
borrow
café
call
candle
card game

celebrate
celebration
driving test
enjoy
enjoy sth
favourite
fireworks
free time
fun
get married
get on with
greetings card
guest
have fun
invitation
keep in touch
laugh
letter
like
look after
look like each other
love (n)
love (v)
make friends (with)
mate
meeting
midnight
New Year's Eve
party
phone
phone call
picnic
present
relationship
relax
ring
share
smile
strategy game
talk
text
wedding
weekday
wrong number
year

Greetings

Be my Valentine!
Best wishes!
Congratulations (on …)!
Good luck (in …)!
Happy birthday/anniversary!
Happy Father's/Mother's Day!
Lots of love!
Many happy returns!
Well done (for …)!

Food

Food and drink

alcohol
apple
bacon
banana
biscuit
bottled water
bread
burger
butter
cake
carrot
cereal
cheese
cheeseburger
chips
chocolate
coffee
cola
cream
crisps
dairy products
egg
fish
fizzy drink
flour
fruit
fruit juice
ham
hamburger
hot chocolate
jam
ketchup
lemon
lemonade
lettuce
margarine
meat
milk
mineral water
mint
oil
orange juice
peanut butter
peanuts
piece of fruit
pizza
potato
rice
salad
salad dressing
sandwich
sausage

smoothie
sugar
sushi
sweets
toast
tomato
tuna
vanilla
vegetables
water

Preparing and eating meals

breakfast
cold
cook
cookbook
cooking
delicious
dinner
drink
eat
fried
fry
hot
hunger
hungry
knife
lunch
lunchtime
meal
smell
snack
starve
treat
Yuck!

Healthy and unhealthy eating

animal fat
balanced
calorie
diet
energy
fast food
health
junk food
takeaway
vegetable fat
vegetarian
vitamin

Eating out

bar
café
cafeteria
canteen
fast-food restaurant
order
pizzeria
restaurant
serve
waiter/waitress

Containers/Measures/ Amounts

a bag of
a bar of
a bottle of
a box of
a can of
a carton of
a cup of
a glass of
a jar of
a kilo of
a packet of
a spoonful of
a tin of
a tub of

Shopping and services

Types of shops

bakery
bookshop
chemist's
clothes shop
greengrocer's
newsagent's
shopping centre
supermarket

Going shopping

advertisement
alternative
broken
buy
changing room
checkout
choice
complain

customer
do up
fashion
fashionable
leaflet
letter of complaint
make a choice
online shop
package/packaging
pick up
put down
put on
queue
receipt
second-hand
sell
seller
service
shop
shopper
take back
take off
try on
unfashionable

Payment and prices

50% off
altogether
bank
cent
cheap
cost (v)
cost (n)
credit card
deposit
dollar
euro
expense
expensive
good deal
included in the price
penny/pence
pocket money
pound
purse
rise
wallet

Travelling and tourism

Kinds of holiday

activity holiday
beach holiday
camping holiday
independent holiday
package holiday
summer camp
summer course
touring holiday
working holiday

Accommodation

beach hut
camp
campsite
guesthouse
host family
hotel
single/double bed
single/double room
stay (with someone/
   at a guesthouse)
view (of)

Journey and transportation

arrive
bicycle/bike
boat
bus
car
car park
catch (a bus/tram)
coach
come back
cycle
delayed
destination
drive
ferry
first-class
flight
fly
give someone a lift
hitchhike
motorbike
plane/aeroplane
racing car
railway line

railway station
route
seat
stop (for a rest)
take the train/ferry
tandem
taxi
traffic jam
train
tram
trip
underground

Places

abroad
beach
beauty spa
bench
border
canal
city centre
club
coast
coastal path
palace
park
place of interest
post
restaurant
swimming pool

On holiday

adventure
atmosphere
book
climb
crowd
dangerous
entrance
excursion
experience
guide
local
luggage
organiser
pack
ride
riding a bike
rock climbing
sailing
street
sunny
surfing
take photographs/photos

tour
travel (n)
travel (v)
travel agent
traveller
unpack
visitor
world

Things you need on holiday

bag
brochure
camera
cool box
map
passport
postcard
rail ticket
rucksack
sleeping bag
souvenir
suitcase
sunglasses
tent
visa

Location and giving directions

across the road
centre
close (to sth)
corner
distance
east
far
get lost
go/walk past sth
in front of
in the north-west/south-east/
    centre
long way away
near
north
on your left/right
opposite
over there
south
straight on
take the first/second turning
    on the left/right
to the end
turn left/right (at)
via
west

Culture

Music and dance

band
boy band
concert
concert hall
dance
dancer
dancing
disco
drums
famous
flamenco dancing
flute
instrument
live
lyre
music
musician
new romantic
play the piano/the guitar
sing
singer
songwriter
techno
ticket
world music

Film, theatre and mass media

act
acting
actor
article
be on
celebrity
cinema
comedy
entertainment
film star
interview
news
newspaper
phone-in show
review

Literature and art

craft
gallery
museum
play
poetry

Sport

Types of sport

athletics
baseball
basketball
bowling
canoeing
cycling
diving
football
gymnastics
high jump
hockey
horse-riding
jogging
karate
sailing
skiing
swimming
table tennis
tennis
volleyball
water sports
wrestling

People

champion
(gold) medallist
goalkeeper
runner
sportsman
supporter
swimmer
winner

Places and accessories

baseball bat
bowling alley
golf course
gym
pitch
sports centre
tennis racquet
track
trainers

Doing sports

break the world record
cheering
do sport
exercise (n)

exercise (v)
fast
football season
football team
game
(gold) medal
join a gym
jump
kick-off
lose
marathon
match
Olympic Games
play
practice (n)
race (n)
race (v)
ride a horse
run
score a goal/a point
serve
ski
sports event
sports facilities
swim
throw
tournament
water-ski
win
World Cup
wrestle

Health

Body parts

body
doctor
ear
finger
head
mind
neck
nose
skin

Diseases

allergic (to)
catch a cold
emergency
hospital
sick
spot

Healthy and unhealthy lifestyle

absorb
human
keep fit
life
non-smoker
sauna
smoke
smoker
vitamin pills
well

Science and technology

Electronic machines

calculator
CD player
digital camera
Game Boy
headphones
iPod
mobile (phone)
on stand-by
photo(graph)
plasma TV
press
record
screen
sound
switch off /on
tape
(tele)phone (n)
(tele)phone (v)
television
the 'on' button
turn off
turn on
video (cassette)
video (recorder)
voicemail

Computers and the Internet

blog
bookmark
check your emails
click on an icon
close/open a window/program
comment
computer game

download/upload music
email
entry
floppy disk
graphics
home computer
information
Internet access
Internet connection
laptop
memory
message
online
palmtop
PC
post
print out
processor
put in/take out the CD/disk
save the document/changes
send
website
wi-fi Internet
word processor
World Wide Web

Technology

advanced
astronomical clock
battery
build
design
electric
fix
future
institute
invent
invention
inventor
light (adj)
light (n)
make
measure
metal
model
modern
neuron
old-fashioned
part
petrol
plastic
pocket
project
safe
science
scientist

99

shape
silver
simple
slim
smart
steel
strong
sun
technique
technological
useful
weigh
weight
wind-up

Numbers and measures

about 3 centimetres long/wide/
  high/thick
billion
centimetre
gram
kilometre
length
litre
metre
millimetre
million
per hour
pound
second
thousand
tonne

Nature and environment

Landscape

air
area
clean
countryside
farm
field
forest
grow
hill
island
jungle
mountain
ocean
oxygen
plant (n)
plant (v)

rainforest
river
sea
space
summer
tree
weather
wind
winter

Animals

animal conservation
bark
bite
cat
cheetah
cow
crocodile
dog
dolphin
donkey
elephant
farm animals
kangaroo
koala
lion
monkey
panda
penguin
pet
pig
poodle
sheep
spider
tiger
whale
wild animals

Protecting the environment

ban
cans
chemicals
clean energy
climate change
cut down
cycle lane
degree (Celsius)
die out
disappear
electricity
endangered
environment
extinction
food shortage

glass
green
litter
packaging
paper
pesticides
petrol
planet
plastic bag
pollute
pollution
produce
protect (against)
public transport
recycle
recycling bin
recycling scheme
reduce
resources
rubbish
save
species
survive
temperature
throw away
traffic jam
waste

State and society

Countries, nationalities and regions

Africa
Asia
Aztecs
Brazil
Brazilian
China
Chinese
The Czech Republic
Denmark
Egypt
Egyptian
Europe
France
French
German
Germany
Greek
Hungarian
Hungary
Indonesia
Italian

Italy
Jamaica
Japan
Japanese
Latin America
Mexico
Middle East
Morocco
Moscow
Peru
Poland
Polish
Portuguese
Romania
Russia
Russian
Singapore
Spain
Spanish
Switzerland
Thailand
the Alps
Turkey
Turkish

Political and social life

ban
capital city
charity
competition
consist of
developed world
donate
euro
first language
foreign language
freedom
from all over the world
fund
international
law
local community
make (a lot of) money
member
national dress
nationality
NATO
official language
organisation
police
poor
president
problem
republic
reward
rich

spend
the European Union
town/city council
traditional food
volunteer (n)
volunteer (v)
world
(world) population

English-speaking countries

American
Australia
Belfast
Bonfire Night
Britain
Cambridge
Canada
Cardiff
Chicago
dollar
Edinburgh
England
English
India
Indian
Ireland
Irish
Leeds
London
Manchester
Mount Rushmore
New Zealand
Northern Ireland
Oxford University
penny/pence
pound
pub
royal family
Scotland
Scottish
South Africa
South Dakota
state
Sydney
Thanksgiving
the UK
the USA
Wales
Welsh
Washington
Washington, D.C.

People

1 Match the words in the left column with the personal information in the right column.

	first name	[c]	**a**	fair
1	surname	☐	**b**	single
2	sex	☐	**c**	John
3	age	☐	**d**	green
4	nationality	☐	**e**	doctor
5	job	☐	**f**	Penzance
6	born in	☐	**g**	male
7	marital status	☐	**h**	British
8	weight	☐	**i**	Jones
9	hair	☐	**j**	34
10	eyes	☐	**k**	80 kilos

2 Complete the text with the correct opposites.

OPPOSITES ATTRACT!

PEOPLE VERY OFTEN LOOK FOR PARTNERS WHO ARE NOT SIMILAR, BUT VERY DIFFERENT! You can see it in appearance and personality. Very attractive people often have ____ugly____ partners. Tall men often have ¹_____ wives, slim women usually prefer ²_____ men. If your hair is curly, your boyfriend will probably have ³_____ hair. ⁴_____ people choose right-handed partners. You can be even fashion opposites. Men who like wearing suits often choose women who wear ⁵_____ clothes. Responsible women have ⁶_____ husbands and ⁷_____ girls have confident boyfriends. It is interesting how many hard-working men have ⁸_____ wives.

3 Complete the missing words on the conference name tags.

name: Heinrich Hans
country: ____Germany____
nationality: ____German____

3 name: Kim Su
country: __J_____
nationality: __J_____

1 name: María Morales
country: __S_____
nationality: __S_____

4 name: Natasha Nabokov
country: __R_____
nationality: __R_____

2 name: Valmont Valbon
country: __F_____
nationality: __F_____

5 name: Szabrina Szabo
country: __H_____
nationality: __H_____

4 Circle the correct answers.

When it is raining, you need
a a swimsuit.
b sunglasses.
(c) an umbrella.

1 A bald person has no
a hair.
b money.
c clothes.

2 You wear an evening dress
a when you go to sleep.
b for a techno party.
c for an official party.

3 Trainers are some kind of
a shoes.
b trousers.
c shorts.

4 People who like giving money to others are
a rude.
b generous.
c careful.

5 Easy-going people
a don't get annoyed easily.
b are often in a bad mood.
c get bored easily.

6 Which of these are accessories?
a blue jumpers
b woollen cardigans
c leather belts

7 You can wear a coat
a on your ears.
b on your body.
c on your hand.

8 When your hair is light brown, it is
a almost black.
b as brown as dark chocolate.
c not as brown as dark chocolate.

9 A 'glamorous' person is
a very clever.
b very beautiful.
c very funny.

10 Your friend has borrowed money from you and doesn't want to give it back. How do you feel?
a excited
b glad
c angry

11 You usually wear boots
a on the beach.
b in the snow.
c at home.

Home

1 Look at the picture. Read the description of a room and correct six mistakes.

                                        living room
The biggest room in our house is the ~~study~~.

When we were young, we rode our bicycles in

there, but now there is too much furniture. In

the room there is a cooker and a clock on the

wall. On the right there is a big sofa and in the

middle there is a big wardrobe and a desk next

to it. Next to the desk there are some shelves

and a radio above them. On the right there is

a small, round table.

2 Complete the diagram with words from the box.

> basin cooker bed desk fridge sink
> washing machine shower telephone
> ~~microwave~~ bath chair clock wardrobe

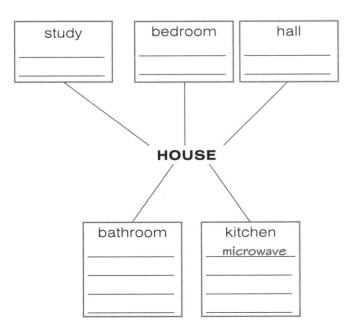

3 Circle the correct answers.

What do we do in the dining room?
a sleep (**b**) eat **c** have a bath

1 Which is the most peaceful?
a a village **b** a town **c** a city

2 A cosy room is usually
a modern and unusual.
b small and comfortable.
c enormous and noisy.

3 Windows are usually made of
a plastic and paper. **c** wood and glass.
b paper and metal.

4 Where can you see an attic?
a upstairs **c** outside the house
b downstairs

5 Which of these isn't typically peaceful?
a disco **c** bedroom
b shopping centre

6 Traffic jams don't happen in
a streets. **b** parks. **c** cities.

7 Where can you find grass?
a on the floor **c** above the door
b in the garden

8 Where can you do the shopping?
a in a museum **c** in a market square
b in a church

9 You have a house-warming party when you
a buy a flat.
b sell a flat.
c have a new neighbour.

10 When a house is for rent it means
a it has no owner.
b somebody can buy it.
c somebody will live there and pay its owner.

11 Your next-door neighbour lives in
a your apartment. **c** your building.
b the building opposite.

4 Read the names and decide what kinds of places they refer to.

Camden, Grand Bazaar, Portobello	_market_
1 Las Ramblas, Downing, Fifth Avenue	s_____
2 Red, Trafalgar, Pigalle	s_____
3 Swiss, CITI, World, Millennium	b_____
4 Auchan, Tesco, Leclerc	s_____
5 Marriott, Ritz, Holiday Inn	h_____
6 Central, Hyde, Regent's	p_____
7 Hermitage, Prado, Louvre	m_____

103

School

1 Complete the quiz with the correct words, then answer the questions. Count the symbols and read the solution!

What kind of student are you?

1 Tomorrow you are going to take an important exam.
  a You s<u>tudy</u> a lot. □
  b You don't do anything because you are sure you will p_____ it. ★
  c You don't do anything because you are sure you will f_____ it (or you simply forget about it). ✿

2 In primary school
  a you always did your h_____. □
  b you were always l_____ for school. ✿
  c you couldn't c_____ because you were bored. ★

3 What do you like best?
  a school e_____ – you like visiting interesting places with your friends. ✿
  b taking exams and getting good g_____ – you are the happiest person when you get an A! □
  c finding solutions to d_____ problems. ★

4 You think
  a you will l_____ school as soon as possible because it is a waste of time. ★
  b you will go to university and do a d_____. □
  c basic e_____ is enough to be successful. ✿

5 You always lose
  a your n_____ (but even if you have it you hardly ever take notes). ★
  b your t_____ so you never know what lessons you are going to have. ✿
  c your d_____, but it doesn't matter – all these words are in your head. □

Solution

Which symbol appears most often in your answers?

□ You are a typical 'A' student. Your notebooks are well organised and you get good marks. But don't forget about your friends and hobbies!

✿ You like school because your friends also go there. Sometimes you think lessons aren't very interesting. Remember that you can do well if you are doing something creative!

★ Good news! You might be a genius! You are so intelligent that you get bored at school. But remember that even a genius must have basic education!

2 Below you will find fragments of textbooks from different subjects. Write the names of the subjects.

Ethanol: C_2H_5OH is a substance which contains an OH group …
  <u>Chemistry</u>

1 The brain, which weighs about three pounds, is one of the biggest and most important organs of the human body. _____

2 Monet painted his 'Impression: soleil levant' in the spring of 1872: the sun seen through the mist quickly became a symbol of Impressionism. _____

3 The second driest area in the world is the Atacama Desert in northern Chile. _____

4 The war went on for six years, but finally ended with the battle of Berlin. _____

5 We use the Past Simple to talk about actions and states in a finished period of time. _____

6 A triangle is a geometric figure with three sides and three angles, which can be the same or different. _____

7 In Shakespeare's *Macbeth*, the character of Lady Macbeth is particularly interesting. In Act 1 scene 3 she tells her husband … _____

3 Circle the correct answers.

The word 'book' is
  a an adjective.
  b a verb.
  (c) a noun.

1 In physical education you learn about
  a planets.   **c** sports.
  b plants.

2 A uniform is something you can
  a learn.   **c** wear.
  b pass.

3 Which is not a part of Maths?
  a Economics
  b Calculus
  c Trigonometry

4 When will you have your graduation party?
  a when you start school
  b after you finish school
  c just before the exams

5 It is in your schoolbag.
  a a textbook
  b a classroom
  c a degree

6 The word 'beginner' describes
  a a subject.   **c** a level.
  b a degree.

7 Departments are found
  a in a primary school.
  b in a sports club.
  c at a university.

8 A typical 'F' student gets
  a good grades.
  b bad grades.
  c a degree.

9 You can find a message board
  a in a book.
  b on a computer.
  c on the wall.

10 You take school-leaving exams
  a during the academic year.
  b to get a certificate.
  c after you start university.

11 You can do it, take it or enrol on it.
  a a college
  b graduation
  c a course

Work

1 What do the people doing these jobs have in common? Use the ideas from the box.

> wear a uniform   be good with money
> ~~be good with their hands~~
> work outside   be good with children
> have special equipment

    hairdresser, cake decorator

    <u>They are good with their hands.</u>

1 flight attendant, policeman

_____

2 gardener, lifeguard

_____

3 babysitter, teacher

_____

4 dentist, window cleaner

_____

5 manager, shop assistant

_____

2 Look at the pictures. Guess which people need these objects for their work.

   <u>singer</u>   **4** f_____

1 c_____   **5** d_____

2 b_____   **6** a_____

3 n_____   **7** s_____

3 Complete the text from the Letters to Susan problem page in the 'Modern and Beautiful' magazine with words from the box.

> ambitions   application forms   companies
> employ   interviews   job   job centre   licence
> some money   skills   ~~unemployed~~   well
> workers   work experience

Dear Susan,

I am really unhappy because I have been <u>unemployed</u> for three years and I am still looking for a ¹_____ ! I have had twenty-four ²_____ and I have filled in about a hundred ³_____. I have some ⁴_____ : three years ago I worked as a receptionist in a hotel. Every month I go to the ⁵_____, but nobody wants to ⁶_____ me. I know that ⁷_____ need ⁸_____, so is there something wrong with me? People say I am quite pretty and intelligent, I speak English ⁹_____, I have a driving ¹⁰_____ and some computer ¹¹_____. When I was younger, I had some ¹²_____ – I wanted to be famous and rich, but now I would just like to earn ¹³_____ ... Please, help, because I'm starting to think there is no hope ...

Jane

4 Circle the correct answers.

   A waiter often works
   a outside.   **(b)** at weekends.   **c** in the office.

1 Which of these is typically a part-time job?
   a fruit picker   **b** taxi driver   **c** doctor

2 When you look for your first job, you don't need any
   a qualifications. **b** skills.   **c** work experience.

3 An employer is somebody who
   a gives a job.   **b** gets a job.   **c** applies for a job.

4 Your current employment is
   a a job you're looking for.
   b where you work.
   c all your work experience.

5 I don't like the idea of wearing uniforms, so I want to work as
   a a policeman/policewoman
   b a teacher   **c** a nurse

6 A pilot works
   a in a factory.
   b in the fashion industry.   **c** at an airport.

7 Which of these must be good with animals?
   a a vet   **b** a soldier   **c** a window cleaner

Family and social life

1 Put the words and expressions in the logical order.

in the evening, in the morning, at night, in the afternoon

<u>in the morning   in the afternoon   in the evening   at night</u>

1 become old, be young, die, be middle-aged

_____

2 have an argument, buy a present, be mad at somebody, apologise

_____

3 be a teenager, have grandchildren, be a child, be an adult

_____

4 go to bed, go to work, have lunch, get dressed

_____

5 in the sixties, last summer, in 1954, last night

_____

2 Complete the text with the verbs from the list.

begin   chat   drive   finish   ~~get~~   go (3x)   have   listen
play   read   relax   ride   take (2x)   clean   watch

Time for sleeping

My biggest problem is that a day has only 24 hours. I ___get___ dressed in fifteen minutes. I ¹_____ work at nine o'clock and I ²_____ at five – that's eight hours. I ³_____ to work and back in the car – that's two hours. I ⁴_____ my dog for a walk twice a day – about an hour for that. I ⁵_____ breakfast, lunch and dinner (one hour), I ⁶_____ a shower twice a day (half an hour). I also have some hobbies. After work I ⁷_____ computer games or I ⁸_____ on the Internet (two hours). I ⁹_____ to the radio (one hour). I also ¹⁰_____ my bike or ¹¹_____ to the cinema (two hours). Unfortunately, I ¹²_____ television a lot (two hours). Before I ¹³_____ to bed I always ¹⁴_____ a book (one hour). I also ¹⁵_____ shopping and ¹⁶_____ my flat (two hours), and then I just ¹⁷_____ (fifteen minutes). I have counted: all these routine activities take me 23 hours – so how much time is left for sleeping?

3 What celebrations do the pictures refer to?

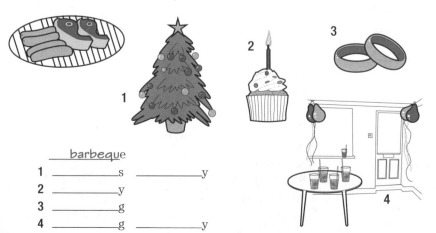

_____barbeque_____
1 _____s _____y
2 _____y
3 _____g
4 _____g _____y

4 Circle the correct answers.

August is in
a winter.   **b** spring.   **c** summer.

1 Which of these is not a toy?
a a ball   **b** a stamp
c a teddy bear

2 Who is your nephew?
a your brother
b your sister's daughter
c your brother's son

3 If your mother gets married again, her husband is your
a stepfather.
b uncle.
c flatmate.

4 Your grandmother's grandchild cannot be
a your brother.
b your cousin.
c your niece.

5 What can you collect?
a dolls
b the Internet
c tennis

6 I'm giving a party next week and I have to write invitation
a papers.
b pieces.
c cards.

7 Your aunt's mother is your
a cousin.
b grandmother.
c stepmother.

8 What can't you do with a child?
a adopt
b grow
c look after

9 On New Year's Eve you are probably not going to
a see fireworks.
b go out with your friends.
c shop for Christmas presents.

10 Which of these is in autumn?
a February
b July
c October

11 Your nephew is your
a brother's son.
b sister's daughter.
c uncle's son.

Food, shopping and services

1 Complete the text with the correct words.

GOOD PLANS

Lisa planned to go shopping for the right things: some healthy food that would not make her fat. But you shouldn't do the shopping when you are hungry! And Lisa was very hungry. She wanted to buy some breakfast ___cereals___, but she bought some delicious [1]b_____ instead. They would be perfect with her morning coffee. She planned to buy [2]m_____ w_____ to drink, but she thought the [3]f_____ d_____ were more exciting, so she bought some. She decided to get some [4]s_____ – meat for energy! What could she have with them? Not [5]p_____, she wouldn't have time to boil them. So she bought some [6]c_____ instead – easy and the same thing really. There weren't any nice [7]a_____ or oranges, so she bought a jar of [8]j_____. She planned to buy ten [9]e_____ and a bag of [10]f_____ to make an omelette for dinner, but she was so hungry that she left the supermarket and went to a fast-food restaurant. She had a cheeseburger and chips. Lovely!

2 Which dishes are you going to make?

I need flour, sugar, eggs and butter. I'm going to make a c a k e .

1 I need flour and water. I'm going to make b _ _ _ _ .

2 I need potatoes and oil. I'm going to fry c _ _ _ _ .

3 I need cheese, ham and some ketchup. I'm going to eat a p _ _ _ _ .

4 I need lettuce, tomatoes and tuna. I'm going to have a s _ _ _ _ .

5 I need bread, ham and butter. I'm going to eat a s _ _ _ _ _ _ _ .

3 Put the words and expressions in the logical order.

read a cookbook, make a big meal, be hungry

be hungry   read a cookbook   make a big meal

1 leave a tip, order food, meet for dinner

_____

2 take back, find a receipt, pay

_____

3 mix potatoes and tuna, boil potatoes, add tuna

_____

4 lose a purse, go shopping, spend lots of money

_____

4 Circle the correct answers.

Which of these can't you buy in a tin?
(a) bread   **c** ham
b tuna

1 Before you buy a skirt, you will try it
a in.   **b** out.   **c** on.

2 In a queue there are
a sales assistants.
b customers.
c prices.

3 Which of these is not a typical takeaway?
a pizza
b chips
c chocolate

4 Butter is a kind of
a bread.
b sandwich.
c dairy product.

5 Where can you buy a newspaper?
a at a chemist's
b at a newsagent's
c at a bookshop

6 If you can get a good deal, it means that
a it's better not to buy the thing.
b the thing you buy is too expensive.
c you get a good price.

7 When you fry, you don't use
a water.
b oil.
c butter.

8 You complain about something when you are
a happy about it.
b unhappy about it.
c glad with it.

9 You will not find a changing room
a in a clothes department.
b in a shopping centre.
c in a leaflet.

10 Which of these doesn't matter when you buy shoes?
a price
b size
c taste

107

Travelling and tourism

1 Complete the postcards with words from the boxes. Name the types of holiday.

1

~~arrived~~   booked   brochure   crowded   delayed   transfer

Dear Tom,

We ___arrived___ yesterday. We were so tired! The flight was
¹_____ and the airport was really ²_____. We waited two
hours for the bus ³_____ to the hotel. The room that we
⁴_____ is not exactly like the one in the ⁵_____ – it's
smaller and there is no view at all. And the beach is three kilometres
from the hotel! Can you imagine?

Love!

Mum and Dad

Type of holiday: _package_ holiday

2

coach   exciting   guide   guidebook   seats   stay

Dear Tom,

It's lovely here in Italy! We were in Venice on Tuesday, then Florence
and today we will be in Rome. We always ¹_____ in very good
hotels, but there's a lot of travelling. The ²_____ is
air-conditioned, but the ³_____ are not very comfortable. Our
⁴_____ is very nice and tells wonderful stories, we've seen a lot
of ⁵_____ places that I haven't read about in my ⁶_____ !

Love!

Granny

Type of holiday: t_____ holiday

3

local tradition   danced   guesthouse   missed   souvenir   travelled

Hi Tom!

Spain is absolutely wonderful! We have ¹_____ to so many places!
Barcelona is beautiful: we've seen Sagrada Familia and we ²_____
the night away (a very strange ³_____ here is that a lot of clubs
open at midnight!). In the morning we were so tired that we
⁴_____ the bus to Madrid! We went to the seaside instead, and
we stayed in a very nice ⁵_____ . We bought a funny ⁶_____
for you.

Kisses!

Susan and Jim

Type of holiday: s_____ holiday

4

bag   blanket   campsite   hostel   scenery   tent

Hi Tom!

The ¹_____ is beautiful here – there's an old, dark forest and
a wide stream with clear, mountain water. But probably it's not going to
be a holiday of my dreams! The ²_____ where we are staying is
ugly. Today it's cold and it's raining all the time, and we're sitting in our
wet ³_____ . My sleeping ⁴_____ is wet and yesterday
somebody stole my ⁵_____ , so I think I'll catch a cold if we don't
find a youth ⁶_____ tomorrow. I hope you are not so unlucky ...

See you soon.

David

Type of holiday: c_____ holiday

2 Circle the correct answer.

Which of these is not
a souvenir?
a a mug
b a key ring
c a beach house

1 Which of these do you not
find at the airport?
a a flight attendant
b a plane
c a ferry

2 You practise canoeing
a on the rocks.
b on water.
c on the ground.

3 What do you do when you
hitchhike?
a you drive on your own
b you travel with a travel
company
c you get free transport
from other drivers

4 When your flight is
cancelled, it means that
a you must wait for it.
b you must hurry up.
c you must look for another
flight.

5 Which of these is not
connected with the beach?
a a coastal path
b sunglasses
c traffic jam

6 An adventure is something
a boring.
b exciting.
c usual.

7 When you give someone
a lift, you
a use a boat.
b take someone in your car.
c usually go abroad.

8 Which country is not a
typical destination for a
package holiday?
a Greece   b Spain   c Russia

9 When you go on independent
holiday, it means you
a go on a package tour.
b go to a summer camp.
c organise your holiday
on your own.

10 You cannot travel by
a coach.   b station.   c train.

Culture

1 Match the descriptions with the people.

dancer   [j]

1 songwriter □
2 film star □
3 film director □
4 singer □
5 musician □
6 celebrity □
7 reporter □
8 artist □
9 writer □

a plays an instrument

b is a famous person

c uses watercolours

d is good at story telling

e tells the news on TV or on the radio

f gives instructions to actors and camera crew

g famous actor or actress who plays the main part in a film

h records songs in a recording studio

i writes the words and sometimes the music of songs

j dances in a musical

2 Read the sentences. Who or what are they talking about?

Most girls like them because they are handsome, but I love their dancing and singing.
b**oy** b**and**

1 'I loved it – Peter Jackson's my favourite director'.
f_____

2 The Spanish music was fantastic and the dance just wonderful!
f_____ d_____

3 'The acting was briliant!'
t_____

4 My favourite kind of it? It's definitely cinema!
e_____

5 I listen to one when driving to work, but I'm too shy to take part in it myself.
p_____ – i_____

6 I think the questions were too personal and that's why the actress didn't want to answer them.
i_____

3 Complete the text with the correct words from the box.

advertisement article cover edition
heading ~~journalist~~ magazine newspaper

MISTAKES CAN HAPPEN

I am a _journalist_ and I work for a [1]_____. We often have a good laugh about the strange things that happen. Once I wrote an [2]_____ about the new government, but somebody put the wrong [3]_____ above it. It said: New government – new allergy! I guess what the journalist wanted was 'new energy'! It's just that we are always in a hurry ... Sometimes I write news stories for a fashion [4]_____ too. One month we had a fantastic photo for the front [5]_____ – it showed a woman with beautiful gold earrings. Next to her there were big letters saying "Wear old!" because the 'g' was missing ... And yesterday, in the Sunday [6]_____ of our newspaper we had an interview with a politician who is bald, and next to it there was an [7]_____ of some medicine that makes your hair grow!

4 Tick true and cross false. Correct the false sentences.

You can see pictures in a gallery.   ✓

'Top Ten' is a list of best galleries.   ✗
It's a list of records.

1 You can see the news in a theatre. □
_____

2 You can find musicians in a concert hall. □
_____

3 You can see a concert in a magazine. □
_____

4 Advertisements inform you about events. □
_____

5 If the show was brilliant it means that you didn't like it. □
_____

6 Poetry is science. □
_____

7 A book can come out. □
_____

8 The lyre is a very modern instrument. □
_____

109

Health and sport

1 Write the appropriate sports next to the sportsmen's names. Write the correct names of the sports equipment in the pictures and match them with the proper sport.

Babe Ruth

Hank Aaron

Satchel Page   b a s e b a l l

[c] baseball bat

a

1 Wayne Gretzky

Sergei Fedorov

Mariusz Czerkawski   i _ _ h _ _ _ _ _

☐ _____

b

2 Jerzy Dudek

Pele

Zinedine Zidane   f _ _ _ _ _ _

☐ _____

c

3 Boris Becker

Pete Sampras

Martina Navratilova   t _ _ _ _ _

☐ _____

d

2 Circle the right answers.

Which of these is not associated with football?

(a) bowling alley **b** team   **c** supporter

1 Which of these belongs to athletics?

a judo   **b** volleyball   **c** high jump

2 You cannot beat

a a player.   **b** a record.   **c** a race.

3 Which of these is a name for both people and shoes?

a goalkeepers **b** trainers   **c** footballers

4 A kick-off starts

a the Olympic Games.
b a football match.
c a judo competition.

5 Which of these is not a team sport?

a volleyball   **b** table tennis **c** baseball

6 You cannot score

a a medal.   **b** a goal.   **c** a point.

7 Which of these is typically a water sport?

a football   **b** cycling   **c** canoeing

3 Complete the Internet Diary with words from the boxes.

| feel | have | join | keep | ~~weigh~~ | work |

Monday, 28th December

Oh dear! Christmas is over and I have never been so fat. I _weigh_ more than my mother!
I [1]_____ awful. In the evening I'm going to
[2]_____ the gym – it will [3]_____ me active.
I decided to [4]_____ with a personal trainer –
I hope at least he will be handsome. And I will
[5]_____ a sauna – I've heard it really makes you slim!

| calories | class | machines |
| allergy | relax | stress |

Tuesday, 29th December

It was awful yesterday! My personal trainer was middle-aged and bald. I went to an exercise
[6]_____ with music but I felt like a dancing elephant. I tried the exercise [7]_____ (they are too complicated for me). Last night I couldn't sleep. I'm sure it was because of [8]_____. Perhaps I have an [9]_____ to aerobics. I don't think I'll go to the gym today. And now, I must have some chocolate. I know it has a lot of [10]_____, but it helps me to
[11]_____ …

| aspirin | serious | helps | catch | sick |
| headache | | | | |

Wednesday, 30th December

This morning I decided to go jogging. It was stupid of me because I was wearing only a T-shirt, and it started to snow. I always [12]_____ a cold in the winter but this time it's really [13]_____! I am so
[14]_____ and I have a [15]_____. I took an
[16]_____ but it didn't help. I must have something good to eat – it always [17]_____!

| alcohol | chocoholic | food | pills |
| reduces | smoke | | |

Thursday, 31st December, New Year's Eve

I had a big pizza yesterday and I feel better!
It's the last day of the year, so it's definitely time for some decisions.
In the new year
1 I won't drink [18]_____.
2 I won't eat sweets (although I'm a [19]_____!).
3 I will walk everywhere because it [20]_____ stress.
4 I will take vitamin [21]_____.
5 I will not [22]_____.
6 I will not eat fast [23]_____. (But there were some nice hamburgers in the fridge … It's OK to have just one, with some chips … After all, I'm going to change my life tomorrow, so I need to be strong …)

Science and technology

1 Complete the advertisements for new products with words from the boxes. Complete the names of the products.

---
off ~~on~~ out to

1

Tired of typing all those letters and reports? Try **SuperTalk** – it switches ___on___ automatically when you touch it! You don't have to type: you just dictate into the machine what you want to have on paper, and it will print it [1]_____ immediately. To switch it [2]_____ just say: 'Goodbye'. **SuperTalk**: brilliant and easy [3]_____ use. **SuperTalk** – the best P_____ that money can buy!

---
camera invention ring

2

Don't miss this if you're a gadget addict! Over two hundred [1]_____ tones and a high-quality [2]_____ to take pictures. The best human [3]_____ since the times of the wheel! **Sambor** – the latest M_____ P_____ !

---
check click download electricity
memory mobile

3

You can take this everywhere: it needs no [1]_____ . You can [2]_____ as much as you want: it has an enormous [3]_____ . You can [4]_____ your emails on the train – it is a [5]_____ computer. Just [6]_____ on 'Go' and enter a new world – the world of **TANAKA** – the new L_____ C_____!

---
buttons turn press watch

4

If you feel television is not enough, try the new **MOVIEMASTER**! Just [1]_____ its special [2]_____ to [3]_____ it on. With the new DVD Master you will [4]_____ all the latest films! D_____ P_____

2 Match the words and label the pictures.

plasma   b   **a** player
1 computer   ☐   **b** TV
2 microwave   ☐   **c** disk
3 CD   ☐   **d** oven
4 digital   ☐   **e** camera
5 floppy   ☐   **f** game

A _____   B _____   C _____

D _____   E _plasma_   F _____
            _TV_

3 Circle the right answers.

You use a digital camera
a to take photos under water.   **c** to do photos.
b to make photos.

1 A washing machine is
a a sink.   **b** an invention.   **c** a dishwasher.

2 A screen is
a a part of a computer.
b a kind of web page in the Internet.
c an Internet friend.

3 You use a remote control to
a type letters.   **b** print documents.
c change channels.

4 When you stop watching TV, you should … your TV set off.
a use   **b** connect   **c** turn

5 When you upload something on your computer, it means you
a move it from your PC to a computer network.
b you print it.
c move it from a network to your PC.

6 Which of these does not use electricity?
a a lamp   **b** a wheel   **c** a microwave oven

7 Maria Skłodowska-Curie was a famous
a writer.   **b** poet.   **c** scientist.

Nature and environment

1 Complete the text with the correct form of the expressions from the box.

be in danger   cut down trees
grow plants   save animals
pollute the environment
recycle rubbish

ECO-FRIENDS

The earth is in danger!
We must do something!
Big factories ¹_____!
If we don't do anything, the air will be so dirty
that we will not be able to breathe!
People ²_____ in rainforests!
If we don't stop them, we will live in the world
without animals and plants.
Our organisation helps to ³_____,
such as wild tigers and whales.
We ⁴_____ and produce new materials
such as paper and glass,
we also ⁵_____ in greenhouses
so that we can save the forests.

Be eco-friendly!
Join us!
The world depends on your decision!

2 Circle the correct answers.

Which of these is a wild animal?
a a sheep   **b** a cow   **c** an elephant

1 You cannot recycle
a litter.   **b** oxygen.   **c** plastic bags.

2 Which of these is not made of water?
a rain   **b** snow   **c** wind

3 The sun sets in the
a west.   **b** east.   **c** north.

4 Cheetahs are bigger than
a whales.   **b** elephants.   **c** spiders.

5 Which of these is not a typical pet?
a a mouse   **b** a donkey   **c** a cat

6 Extinction is a situation when
a certain animals or plants die out.
b the number of certain animals or plants grows.
c certain animals or plants become stronger.

7 Which of these barks?
a a cat   **b** a dog   **c** a cow

8 A volunteer is a person who
a likes helping others and doesn't expect any payment.
b doesn't like helping others.
c is paid regular money for helping others.

9 There are so few tigers now that they could die
a off.   **b** up.   **c** out.

3 Write the correct geographical categories (a) next to the names below. Then add one example (b) to each category, choosing from the list.

the Dead Sea   Canberra   Crete   Europe   Indian
France   Hudson   Taiga   Pyrenees   Thames

	a ___bay___	of Biscay San Francisco b ___Hudson___
1	a _____	Africa Australia b _____
2	a _____	Italy Germany b _____
3	a _____	Sherwood the Amazon Jungle b _____
4	a _____	the Alps the Apennines b the _____
5	a _____	Titicaca Balaton b _____
6	a _____	the Pacific the Atlantic b the _____
7	a _____	the Amazon the Nile b the _____
8	a _____	Rome Moscow b _____
9	a _____	Cuba Madagascar b _____

4 Match the parts of the sentences.

The cheetah has got long legs   **h**

1 The dolphin is a very   ☐

2 Penguins have got wings but   ☐

3 The blue whale is   ☐

4 The poodle is   ☐

5 That poodle is   ☐

6 My dog always   ☐

7 Koala bears climb   ☐

a they cannot fly.

b the largest living animal.

c a kind of dog with curly hair.

d aggressive – it bit me yesterday.

e trees and eat their leaves.

f barks at strangers.

g intelligent sea animal.

h which make it the fastest runner.

State and society, English-speaking countries

1 Complete the diagram with words from the box.

The British Isles   The Republic of Ireland
Scotland   Wales   Belfast   London (3x)
Cardiff   Dublin   The United Kingdom

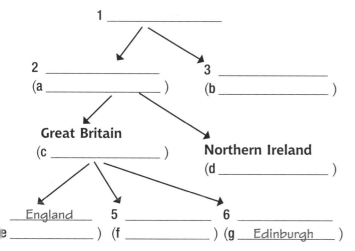

1 _____

2 _____   3 _____
(a _____)   (b _____)

Great Britain
(c _____)

Northern Ireland
(d _____)

England   5 _____   6 _____
e _____) (f _____) (g Edinburgh)

2 Match the words to form compounds and complete the sentences.

charity	e	a	family
1 United	☐	b	Nations
2 official	☐	c	language
3 world	☐	d	year
4 royal	☐	e	organisation
5 gap	☐	f	population

The problem is that people in this part of the country just don't want to speak the _official language_ so it is difficult to communicate.

1 Almost every country in the world belongs to the _____ .

2 These days, many students are choosing to have a _____ and see the world before they start work or further study.

3 He had a very unhappy childhood and when he finally became rich and famous, he started a _____ that collected money for children.

4 A lot of children are born in Africa and Asia, so although people in Europe have fewer children every year, the _____ is going up.

5 In the 90s the British _____ became less popular mainly because of the divorce between Prince Charles and Princess Diana.

3 Complete the table with basic information about Papua New Guinea with words from the box.

area   capital   ~~flag~~   Queen   official
languages   population   Prime Minister

Papua New Guinea

flag	
1 _____	Port Moresby
2 _____	English, Tok Pisin, Hiri Motu
3 _____	Elizabeth II
4 _____	Sir Michael Somare
5 _____	462,840 km²
6 _____	4,927,000

4 Circle the correct answers.

Cornwall is in
a England.   **b** Scotland.   **c** Ireland.

1 You can collect money to _____ it to charity.
  a ban   **b** spend   **c** donate

2 Wales is a country _____ of England.
  a south   **b** west   **c** east

3 You can get a nice _____ for the good things you have done.
  a reward   **b** price   **c** fund

4 UNICEF
  a protects the environment.
  b helps children.
  c cures people.

5 The capital of the USA is
  a New York.
  b Washington.
  c San Francisco.

6 Oxford University is
  a a well-known university in the USA.
  b a modern university in Scotland.
  c an old university in England.

7 There are 51 of these in the USA.
  a national parks
  b cities
  c states

8 We meet every two months to discuss the problems of our
  a population.
  b president.
  c local community.

EXAM VOCABULARY PRACTICE ANSWER KEY

PEOPLE

1 1i 2g 3j 4h 5e 6f 7b 8k 9a 10d
2 1 short 2 fat 3 straight 4 left-handed 5 casual
6 irresponsible 7 shy 8 lazy
3 1 Spain / Spanish 2 France / French
3 Japan / Japanese 4 Russia / Russian
5 Hungary / Hungarian
4 1a 2c 3a 4b 5a 6c 7b 8c 9b 10c 11b

HOME

1 a cooker – a fireplace
On the right – On the left
wardrobe – cupboard
shelves – drawers
a radio – a painting
On the right – On the left
2 study: desk, chair
bedroom: bed, wardrobe
hall: clock, telephone
bathroom: basin, washing machine, shower, bath
kitchen: cooker, fridge, sink
3 1a 2b 3c 4a 5a 6b 7b 8c 9a 10c 11c
4 1 street 2 square 3 bank 4 supermarket 5 hotel
6 park 7 museum

SCHOOL

1 **1 b** pass **c** fail
2 a homework **b** late **c** concentrate
3 a excursions **b** grades **c** difficult
4 a leave **b** degree **c** education
5 a notebook **b** timetable **c** dictionaries
2 1 Biology 2 Art 3 Geography 4 History
5 English 6 Maths 7 Literature
3 1c 2c 3a 4b 5a 6c 7c 8b 9c 10b 11c

WORK

1 1 They wear uniforms. 2 They work outside.
3 They are good with children. 4 They have special
equipment. 5 They are good with money.
2 1 cook 2 builder 3 nurse 4 fire-fighter 5 dentist
6 actor/actress 7 scientist
3 1 job 2 interviews 3 application forms
4 work experience 5 job centre 6 employ
7 companies 8 workers 9 well 10 licence
11 skills 12 ambitions 13 some money
4 1a 2c 3a 4b 5b 6c 7a

FAMILY AND SOCIAL LIFE

1 1 be young – be middle-aged – become old – die
2 be mad at somebody – have an argument – apologise –
buy a present
3 be a child – be a teenager – be an adult – have
grandchildren
4 get dressed – go to work – have lunch – go to bed
5 in 1954 – in the sixties – last summer – last night
2 1 begin 2 finish 3 drive 4 take 5 have 6 take
7 play 8 chat 9 listen 10 ride 11 go 12 watch
13 go 14 read 15 go 16 tidy 17 relax
3 1 Christmas Day 2 birthday 3 wedding
4 housewarming party
4 1b 2c 3a 4c 5a 6c 7b 8b 9c 10c 11a

FOOD, SHOPPING AND SERVICES

1 1 biscuits 2 mineral water 3 fizzy drinks
4 sausages 5 potatoes 6 crisps 7 apples 8 jam
9 eggs 10 flour
2 1 bread 2 chips 3 pizza 4 salad 5 sandwich
3 1 meet for dinner – order food – leave a tip
2 pay – find a receipt – take back
3 boil potatoes – add tuna – mix potatoes and tuna
4 go shopping – spend lots of money – lose a purse
4 1c 2b 3c 4c 5b 6c 7a 8b 9c 10c

TRAVELLING AND TOURISM

1 **1** 1 delayed 2 crowded 3 transfer 4 booked
5 brochure
2 1 stay 2 coach 3 seats 4 guide 5 exciting
6 guidebook; **Type of holiday:** touring holiday
3 1 travelled 2 danced 3 local tradition 4 missed
5 guesthouse 6 souvenir; **Type of holiday:** sightseeing
holiday
4 1 scenery 2 campsite 3 tent 4 bag 5 blanket
6 hostel; **Type of holiday:** camping holiday
2 1c 2b 3c 4c 5c 6b 7b 8c 9c 10b

CULTURE

1 1i 2g 3f 4h 5a 6b 7e 8c 9d
2 1 film 2 flamenco dance 3 theatre 4 entertainment
5 phone-in 6 interview
3 1 newspaper 2 article 3 heading 4 magazine
5 cover 6 edition 7 advertisement
4 1 ✗ – you can see the news on TV 2 ✓ 3 ✗ – you can
see a concert in a concert hall 4 ✗ – advertisements
make you buy a product 5 ✗ – it means that you liked it
very much 6 ✗ – poetry is a form of literary art
7 ✓ – it means, it is published 8 ✗ – the lyre is a very
old instrument

HEALTH AND SPORT

1 1 ice hockey **d** a hockey stick
2 football **b** a (foot)ball
3 tennis **a** a tennis racquet
2 1c 2c 3b 4b 5b 6a 7c
3 1 feel 2 join 3 keep 4 work 5 have 6 class
7 machines 8 stress 9 allergy 10 calories 11 relax
12 catch 13 serious 14 sick 15 headache
16 aspirin 17 helps 18 alcohol 19 chocoholic
20 reduces 21 pills 22 smoke 23 food

SCIENCE AND TECHNOLOGY

1 **1** 1 out 2 off 3 to – printer
2 1 ring 2 camera 3 invention – mobile phone
3 1 electricity 2 download 3 memory 4 check
5 mobile 6 click – laptop computer
4 1 press 2 buttons 3 turn 4 watch – DVD player
2 1f 2d 3a 4e 5c
A CD player **B** computer game **C** microwave oven
D floppy disk **F** digital camera
3 1b 2a 3c 4c 5a 6b 7c

NATURE AND ENVIRONMENT

1 1 pollute the environment 2 cut down trees
3 save animals 4 recycle rubbish 5 grow plants
2 1b 2c 3a 4c 5b 6a 7b 8a 9c
3 1 **a** continent **b** Europe 2 **a** country **b** France
3 **a** forest **b** Taiga 4 **a** mountains **b** Pyrenees
5 **a** lake **b** Dead Sea 6 **a** ocean **b** Indian
7 **a** river **b** Thames 8 **a** city **b** Canberra
9 **a** island **b** Crete
4 1g 2a 3b 4c 5d 6f 7e

STATE AND SOCIETY
ENGLISH-SPEAKING COUNTRIES

1 1 The British Isles 2 The United Kingdom
3 The Republic of Ireland 5 Wales 6 Scotland
a London **b** Dublin **c** London **d** Belfast **e** London
f Cardiff
2 1b 2c 3f 4a 5d
1 United Nations 2 gap year 3 charity organisation
4 world population 5 royal family
3 1 capital 2 official languages 3 Queen
4 Prime Minister 5 area 6 population
4 1c 2b 3a 4b 5b 6c 7c 8c

SELF-ASSESSMENT TESTS ANSWER KEY

TEST 1 | UNITS 1–2

1 1 Spanish 2 English 3 Hungarian 4 Japanese
5 Egyptian

2 1 cousin 2 niece 3 nephew 4 aunt 5 stepfather
6 grandmother

3 1 Her 2 are 3 at 4 get 5 His 6 is 7 In 8 On

4 1 is Gina from 2 does Paula get up
3 is their teacher's name 4 do they go at weekends

5 1 don't work, work 2 isn't, doesn't come
3 studies, doesn't get

6 1 friends 2 parents' 3 are always 4 often go
5 Our 6 His 7 in 8 getting

LISTENING SKILLS

7 1F 2T 3T 4F 5F 6F 7T

READING SKILLS

8 1b 2c 3a 4d 5c 6c

COMMUNICATION

9 1c 2h 3f 4b 5g 6a 7e 8d

TEST 2 | UNITS 3–4

1 1 notebook 2 trainers 3 MP3 player 4 dictionary
5 purse 6 wallet

2 1a 2c 3a 4c 5b 6c 7c

3 1 to 2 but 3 them 4 got 5 with 6 but/and 7 it
8 at

4 1 doesn't have to 2 can't 3 have to 4 has/'s got
5 haven't got 6 can

5 1 Do farmers have to; they do
2 Can your father; he can't
3 Have they got; they haven't
4 Has your school got; it has
5 Does your sister have to; she doesn't

LISTENING SKILLS

6 1c 2b 3c 4b 5a 6b

COMMUNICATION

7 1 afraid 2 course 3 Here 4 fine 5 problem 6 sorry

READING SKILLS

8 1T 2F 3T 4F 5T 6F 7F 8T

TEST 3 | UNITS 5–6

1 1 shelves 2 armchair 3 sink 4 drawer 5 bottles,
packet 6 sandwich, juice

2 1 in 2 above 3 next to 4 under 5 in front of
6 between

3 1c 2a 3c 4b 5a 6a

4 1 How much money do you spend on pizza?; lot
2 How many biscuits do you eat every week?; many
3 Is there a washing machine in your kitchen?; there isn't
4 Are there any plants in your bathroom?; there are

5 1 Do you live in **a** big house?
2 **The** pizzas in this restaurant are lovely!
3 My sister has got **a** new purse.
4 **Computers** are really useful for homework.
5 Where's my book? It's in **the** living room.

LISTENING SKILLS

6 1 a newsagent's 2 yes 3 yes 4 the garden
5 two 6 £200 7 £150

COMMUNICATION

7 1 turn 2 straight 3 past 4 turning 5 corner
6 across

READING SKILLS

8 1e 2b 3h 4f 5i 6a 7c

TEST 4 | UNITS 7–8

1 1 History 2 Maths/Mathematics 3 Literature
4 Physical Education/PE 5 Science

2 1 leave 2 failed 3 degree 4 save 5 grade 6 took
7 messages 8 washing

3 1 were 2 didn't like 3 couldn't 4 played 5 went
6 learnt/learned 7 didn't have 8 met

4 1 How old were you when you got your first bike?
2 Where did you spend your last holiday?
3 Could you use a computer when you were ten?
4 What did your best friend do last night?

5 1 the best 2 cheaper 3 friendlier 4 the newest
5 the hottest 6 better

6 1b 2c 3a 4b 5a 6c

LISTENING SKILLS

7 1g 2a 3d 4f 5b 6e

READING SKILLS

8 1NI 2F 3T 4T 5T 6NI 7T 8F

COMMUNICATION

9 1 I'm so sorry. 2 What's the matter? 3 Don't worry!
4 How was your day? 5 Well done! 6 You look happy!

TEST 5 | UNITS 9–10

1 1 shirt, tie 2 suit 3 sweater 4 sunglasses 5 trousers

2 1 put on 2 Pick (them) up 3 do up 4 Take off
5 take (it) back 6 trying (clothes) on

3 1 are going to play 2 are they going to go
3 is going to do 4 Is he going to fly
5 'm not going to take

4 1 don't have to 2 mustn't 3 should 4 shouldn't
5 don't have to

5 1 Is Becky working 2 do your friends go
3 don't buy 4 are you doing 5 plays 6 are wearing
7 Does your sister study 8 isn't doing

LISTENING SKILLS

6 1F 2NI 3F 4F 5T 6NI 7F

COMMUNICATION

7 1 some information 2 you tell me 3 mean by
4 Shall I 5 give you 6 did you say

READING SKILLS

8 1 a passport 2 European Union 3 airport
4 (Freedownia) pence 5 black taxis 6 afternoon
7 outside

TEST 6 | UNITS 11–12

1 1 skiing 2 athletics 3 volleyball 4 sailing 5 hockey

2 1 recycle 2 plant 3 pollute 4 wastes 5 clean
6 break

3 1 well 2 dangerous 3 quickly 4 easily 5 beautifully

4 1 I think Josh won't win this match, his opponent is
much better.
2 What will the weather be on Sunday?
3 Will people use petrol in 2040?
4 I am sure you won't have any problems with this
exercise, it isn't very difficult.

5 1 already 2 just 4 yet 5 never

6 1 Have you seen 2 did you buy
3 has/'s already beaten 4 won 5 haven't done
6 didn't go

LISTENING SKILLS

7 1 score 2 England 3 a week 4 two players
5 seven goals/times 6 Northern Ireland

READING SKILLS

8 1 buildings and countryside 2 help the environment
3 local farmers 4 forever 5 In 1895
6 (over) three million 7 nothing 8 a sleeping bag

COMMUNICATION

9 1g 2b 3f 4e 5d 6c

SELF-ASSESSMENT TESTS TAPESCRIPTS

TEST 1 | UNITS 1–2

J – Jose, **M** – Martin

J Hello Martin, what's that?

M It's a letter from my family in Germany.

J Where do you live in Germany?

M We live in Bonn. My father is a doctor and my mother is a teacher. I also have a sister, Ewa. She's fifteen.

J Is Germany very different from England?

M Yes, sometimes. My family gets up very early, at 6 o'clock. School starts at 8 in Germany. In England people start school and work at 9. My father usually goes to work at 7.

J Wow. That's early. Do you have breakfast at home?

M Yes, we always have breakfast in the morning.

J What do you do at the weekend?

M We always get up about 9 o'clock and go shopping. Then we often go for a walk. Sometimes, we go to the cinema and we often chat on the Internet. And you?

TEST 2 | UNITS 3–4

M – man, **B** – boy

M Good morning Mr … er … Davies. Please sit down.

B Good morning. Thank you.

M Now, you're interested in a job as Santa Claus at our shop in December.

B Yes, that's right.

M Why do you think you can do this job?

B Well, I know how to work on a computer but I'm not very good at it.

M Yes, but Santa Claus doesn't have to be good with computers. Why do you think you are a good candidate for the job of a Santa Claus?

B Oh yes, … sorry. I'm very good with children. I've got two young brothers and I have to look after them. I know lots of stories and songs. I like children. And …

M Mmm. Very good. Now, you don't look like Santa Claus. You're very young and tall and slim. Santa Claus is old, short and fat.

B I don't think it's a problem. I can find something to make me look old and fat. My mother is a teacher. She teaches young children and I am always Santa Claus at her school.

M Well, alright. Now, in this job you have to work from 8 o'clock in the morning until 9 o'clock in the evening, seven days a week for three weeks. Can you do that?

B Yes, of course. I'm a student. I don't have to go to university after December 3. I've got my Christmas holidays.

M Good, good. Now, one last thing. Can you say 'Ho, ho, ho' like Santa Claus?

B Ho, ho, ho.

M Very good. You're very good at that. Well, have you got any questions?

B Yes. How much money do I get? You see …

TEST 3 | UNITS 5–6

W – woman, **M** – man

W Hello, Sea View Cottages. Can I help you?

M Yes, I'm interested in renting a cottage for the summer and I've got some questions I'd like to ask.

W Certainly, sir. What would you like to know?

M Well, firstly, where exactly are the cottages?

W Do you know Newlyn, sir?

M Yes, I do.

W Well, from the harbour, you go past the post office and the supermarket to Hill Road. There's a newsagent's on the corner. Turn left into Hill Road and Sea View Gardens is the second road on your right. All the cottages there belong to us and you can choose one.

M Is there a good view?

W Oh yes. You can see the harbour and the sea from the living room and the bedrooms. The kitchen has a view of the garden.

M And what are the cottages like inside?

W They've got two bedrooms with beds, armchairs and a table. There's a small, cosy living room with very comfortable armchairs and a sofa, lots of bookshelves and a TV. There's one bathroom with a bath and a shower and a toilet of course. In the kitchen there are lots of cupboards, a fridge and a washing machine, oh and a cooker.

M And there's a garden, you say.

W Oh, yes, it's very beautiful.

M How much is the rent?

W It's £200 a week in July and August and £150 a week from September to June.

M OK, thank you very much for your help.

W You're welcome.

TEST 4 | UNITS 7–8

Speaker 1 The thing I remember was my first day at school. I wasn't sad at all. I wanted to go to school. I was very happy. I went with my mum. I wanted to run but she stopped me. At the gates, when I said goodbye, I could see her trying to hide her eyes. She didn't want me to see her cry.

Speaker 2 I always remember one Christmas. I was ill and couldn't eat any dinner. I was very sad. I was ill for about two weeks and my grandfather bought me a very expensive model aeroplane. I loved aeroplanes. It was great. It could fly. I had it for years. He was great, my grandfather.

Speaker 3 I remember holidays in France. We went every year. We always did the same things. We stayed in the same town, we visited the same places, we bought our food from the same shop every year.
But every year it was wonderful. I loved it and now I always take my children to the same place.

Speaker 4 I remember when I fell off my bike. I hurt my leg and couldn't walk. I didn't know what to do. I remember a car stopped and a woman got out.

She was very friendly and took me home. She gave me some chocolate in the car and a week later she telephoned my parents to ask how I was. She took the bike in the car as well.

Speaker 5 I remember when my brother went to university. I was only ten, he was nineteen. We only had a small house and we always slept in the same bedroom. Now I had my own room. It was great. Well, I was a bit lonely at first but after a week or two I was happy. I moved my brother's things into a cupboard and put all my books and CDs on the shelves and my posters on the wall.

Speaker 6 Well, it's a long time ago. When the war started, that's the Second World War, I was five. I lived near London and in 1940 I went to live with a family in a village. Lots of children left London. Some weren't happy but the family I went to were lovely. They had a daughter my age and we were like sisters. We still are. I loved my four years there. I didn't want to go home.

TEST 5 | UNITS 9–10

P – presenter, **C** – Mr Clive Jessup, **J** – Joel

P Good evening and welcome to our weekly radio phone-in show The World Today. This evening we are asking: Do our young people look worse than in the past? Here in the studio we have Mr Clive Jessup, a clothes shop owner and Joel Fisher, a young actor and musician. You can ring us from 9 o'clock on 0146 21331. My first question is to Mr Jessup. What do you think of young people's fashions?

C Well, what I can see in my shop is that young people don't want to buy suits these days. In my shop, in the past, we had customers of all ages, with lots of young people among them, who wanted something nice to wear on a Saturday evening and they bought suits, shirts and ties. Now nobody wants them. Look at young Joel here, he's wearing the uniform of the young – blue jeans, an old T-shirt and a pair of trainers.

P Joel, what do you say to Mr Jessup? Do you sometimes wear a suit?

J No, not really. I wore one for my sister's wedding. It was my father's. He's got lots of suits. I haven't got any. Mr Jessup doesn't understand that my clothes are important to me. They tell you something. A suit says: 'I want to look like my parents.' My clothes say: 'I don't want to look like my parents.' You can say a lot with clothes. The T-shirt and trainers, for example, tell you what music I like.

P Yes, your trainers also look a bit expensive. Do you spend a lot on clothes?

J Oh, no, not at all. You don't have to buy expensive clothes to say something. On the contrary, I buy most of my clothes in street markets and they are really cheap. But they have a lot of character and they really say something. Not like the clothes in big stores. I agree with Mr Jessup there – when you buy clothes in big stores they are all the same. If you want to say something with your clothes, you have to look somewhere else.

P Mr Jessup. What do you say about that?

C I still think that young people today have no style. And that you cannot say that a T-shirt or trainers can be stylish. A good suit is something that …

J Oh come on …

P All right. Let's hear what our listeners have to say about that. Telephone now to tell us what you think or ask Joel or Mr Jessup a question. The number, once again, is …

TEST 6 | UNITS 11–12

P – presenter, **J** – Jack

P Welcome back to the programme. So, at half time between Liverpool United and Manchester Town, the score is 3-1 to Manchester. In a few minutes we are going to see the goals again but first, I want to talk to Jack Sinclair, the England manager. An exciting game, Jack.

J Yes, Manchester have played very well. They've already scored three goals and I think they're going to score more in the second half. Liverpool have looked very tired. They have played three games this week and you can see that this match is difficult for them.

P What can Liverpool do?

J They must score in the first five minutes of the second half to have any chance in this match. The problem is they haven't done much yet.

P They've scored one goal. They could score more.

J Mmm. I think they were lucky. The Manchester players are faster and better. I think the manager should change two players. The number 4, Smith, is too small. They need a taller, stronger man at the back. Maybe Donald. The number 10, Fletcher, is having a very bad match. He can't run, he can't kick, he can't do anything. Why is he playing? Why hasn't the manager taken him off yet?

P You don't like Fletcher!

J No. But not just today. I've never liked him. I've never seen him play well. I think Liverpool should sell him. He might be OK at a smaller club.

P He's played fifty games for Liverpool and he's scored seven goals. He's only twenty-one and he's already played for Northern Ireland seventeen times.

J That's Northern Ireland. They haven't got many players to choose from. They're not a big country like England.

P They beat England last year and Fletcher scored, I think! Well, the teams are going to come out for the second half soon so let's look at the goals from the first half …

Pearson Education Limited
Edinburgh Gate
Harlow CM20 2JE
and Associated Companies throughout the world
www.pearsonelt.com

First published 2012
Sixth impression 2015

Set in 10.5/11.5pt ITC Century Light

Printed in Malaysia, CTP-PJB

ISBN 978-1-4082-9709-4

Illustrated by: Yane Christensen pages 10, 31, 43, 66, 73, 85, 102, 103, 107; Matthew Dickin pages 25, 27, 68, 105, 106, 110, 111; John@kja pages 27, 37, 41, 54, 68, 74, 110, 111; Tony Richardson page 40; Martin Sanders pages 16, 88; David Semple pages 19, 29, 47, 61; Kath Walker pages 33, 36, 38, 45, 79, 80, 81, 82, 83; Matt Ward pages 43, 44, 46, 59, 60, 85.

Acknowledgements
The authors and publishers would like to thank the following people for their help in the development of this course:
Monika Adamowicz , Magdalena Augustynek, Edyta Bajda-Kowalczyk, Lidia Bajerska, Małgorzata Barczyńska, Agnieszka Batko, Mariusz Bęcławski, Sebastian Bednarz, Agnieszka Biskup, Elżbieta Bobrowska, Kamila Borkowska, Beata Brzostek, Justyna Cholewa, Jadwiga Chrząstek, Dagmara Chudy, Dorota Ciężkowska-Gajda, Ewa Ciok, Elżbieta Ciurzyńska, Barbara Cybuch, Monika Cynar, Elżbieta Czarnogórska, Maria Czechowicz, Ewa Dąbrowska, Jolanta Dąbrowska, Sylwia Dańczak, Lucyna Daniec-Zych, Monika Dargas-Miszczak, Monika Dębska, Agata Demidowicz, Urszula Deszcz, Jolanta Dola-Niewiadomska, Joanna Domańska, KonradDutkowski, Bożena Dypa, Halina Działecka, Jolanta Dziewulska, Marzena Dziurzyńska, Elżbieta Fabisiak, Renata Fijałkowska, Agnieszka Fijałkowska-Grabowiecka, Jagoda Filipecka, Agnieszka Filipowicz-Wesołowska, Agata Fronczak, Małgorzata Gajcy-Czapigo, Hanna Gajewska-Wolna, Dominika Gala, Joanna Galant, Grażyna Garus, Agnieszka Gatz, Katarzyna Gierałtowska, Anna Gil-Kisiecka, Joanna Gładyszewska, Anna Głowacka, Bogusława Godlewska, Michał Gołda, Ewa Goldnik- Ciok, Monika Grabowska-Królik, Jadwiga Greszta, Beata Gromek, Rafał Grynienko, Urszula Guszczyn, Marta Hilgier, Anita Horbat, Joanna Idem, Barbara Iwanicz, Agnieszka Jakubiec, Elżbieta Jaśków, Agnieszka Jastak, Robert Jastrzębski, Anna Jaźwińska, Małgorzata Jedlińska, Małgorzata Jojdziałło-Odrobińska, Magdalena Junkieles, Mirosław Kaczorek, Ewa Kamińska, Ewa Kamka, Agnieszka Karolak, Maciej Karwowski, Magadalena Kica, Anna Kielan, Kazimierz Klekotko, Katarzyna Kłobukowska, Beata Kochanowska, Ewa Komorowska, Magdalena Konczak, Katarzyna Korejwo, Małgorzata Kowal, Anna Kowalewska, Ewa Kubisz, Agnieszka Kucharska-Widera, Anna Kuklik-Petrykowska, Barbara Kurianiuk, Magdalena Kwasiborska, Anna Kwaśniewska, Janina Lachowska, Jadwiga Łakomek, Urszula Langer, Maria Lasek, Celina Łazowska, Julianna Leczkowska, Agata Lesińska-Domagała, Mirosława Letachowicz, Agnieszka Licińska, Agata Lisicka, Magdalena Loska, Bogusław Lubański, Katarzyna Łukasiewicz, Barbara Madej, Agnieszka Michna, Andrzej Mikołajczak, Waldemar Mileszczyk, Anna Milewska, Paweł Mirecki, Selim Mucharski, Denisa Muller, Marzena Muszyńska, Małgorzata Nibor-Grabowska, Joanna Niedbała, Kinga Niemczuk, Anna Nowotka, Sylwia Obłudek, Katarzyna Ochnio, Bożena Ogrodniczek, Przemysław Ogrodowczyk, Ewa Okrasa, Anita Omelańczuk, Barbara Owczarek, Mariola Palcewicz, Łukasz Pielasa, Joanna Pieróg, Joanna Pilecka, Marta Piróg-Riley, Magdalena Płaneta, Mirosława Podgórska, Ewa Prokopowicz, Anna Rabiega, Elżbieta Radulska, Maria Rakowska, Agnieszka Rodak, Grażyna Rusiecka, Sylwia Sawczuk, Ewa Schubert, Mariola Serowy-Ziółkowska, Renata Sitarz, Tomasz Siuta, Ewa Skoczeń,Dorota Sobakiewicz, Roksana Sobieralska, Katarzyna Sobkowicz, Marzanna Stasiak, Barbara Superson, Monika Świerczyńska, Monika Szałwińska, Anna Szuchalska, Wiktor Szwaja, Katarzyna Tobolska, Katarzyna Tokaj, Ewa Toporek- Niemczyk, Beata Trapnell, Ewa Trochimczyk, Dorota Tyburska, Małgorzata Tygielska, Halina Tykocińska, Karolina Urbaniak, Jolanta Walterska, Anna Waluch, Sławomir Wandycz, Joanna Wap, Hanna Wasilewska, Elżbieta Więcław, Grażyna Wilczyńska, Ewa Wiśniewska-Matraszek, Adam Wójcicki, Michał Wójcik, Małgorzata Wolak, Leszek Wolski, Andrzej Woyda, Anna Wroniecka, Katarzyna Zadrożna-Attia, Ewa Zalewska, Joanna Zalewska, Sławomir Zasuński, Sonia Zbraniborska, Eugeniusz Żebrowski, Andrzej Zejdler, Piotr Zemła, Iwona Ziębicka, Barbara Ziębowicz, Maria Zielińska, Anna Ziemińska, Justyna Zubowicz.